Interactive Student Notebook

S0-BEG-128

History Alive!®
The Medieval World and Beyond

TCi™

Chief Executive Officer: Bert Bower

Chief Operating Officer: Amy Larson

Director of Curriculum: Liz Russell

Managing Editor: Laura Alavosus

Editorial Project Manager: Nancy Rogier

Project Editor: Marie Norris

Copyeditor: Ava Hayes

Editorial Associates: Anna Embree, Sarah Sudano

Production Manager: Lynn Sanchez

Art Director: John F. Kelly

Senior Graphic Designer: Christy Uyeno

Graphic Designer: Don Taka

Photo Edit Manager: Margee Robinson

Photo Editor: Elaine Soares

Production Project Manager: Eric Houts

Art Editor: Mary Swab

Audio Director: Katy Haun

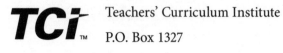

Teachers' Curriculum Institute
P.O. Box 1327
Rancho Cordova, CA 95741

Customer Service: 800-497-6138

www.teachtci.com

ISBN 978-1-58371-917-6

10 11 12 13 14 15 16 -DH- 22 21 20 19 18

Manufactured by Hess Print Solutions, Brimfield, OH
United States of America, September, 2018, Job 273908

Program Director
Bert Bower

Program Author
Wendy Frey

Creative Development Manager
Kelly Shafsky

Contributing Writers
Lillian Duggan
Marisa A. Howard
Barbara Johnson
Christopher Johnson
Rena Korb
Joan Kane Nichols
Joy Nolan

Curriculum Developers
Joyce Bartky
April Bennett
Nicole Boylan
Terry Coburn
Sarah Cook
Julie Cremin
Erin Fry
Amy George
Anne Maloney
Steve Seely
Nathan Wellborne

Reading Specialist
Kate Kinsella, Ed.D.
Reading and TESOL Specialist
San Francisco State University

Teacher Consultants
Terry Coburn
Brookside School
Stockton, California

Randi Gibson
Stanford Middle School
Long Beach, California

Jana Kreger
Hanover Middle School
Hanover, Massachusetts

Dawn Lavond
SC Rogers Middle School
San Jose, California

Michal Lim
Borel Middle School
San Mateo, California

Alana D. Murray
Parkland Middle School
Rockville, Maryland

Stevie Wheeler
Rincon Middle School
San Diego, California

Acknowledgments

Scholars

Dr. William H. Brennan
University of the Pacific

Dr. Philippe Buc
Stanford University

Dr. Eun Mi Cho
*California State University
Sacramento*

Dr. Tom Conlan
Bowdoin College

Dr. Thomas Dandelet
University of California, Berkeley

Dr. James A. Fox
Stanford University

Gloria Frey
*Ethical Culture Schools,
New York*

Christopher Gardner
George Mason University

Dr. Bruce Grelle
California State University Chico

Dr. Kan Liang
Seattle University

Mahan Mirza
University of Notre Dame

Dr. Merrick Posnansky
*University of California,
Los Angeles*

Dr. John Rick
Stanford University

Dr. Melinda Takeuchi
Stanford University

Dr. Allen Wittenborn
San Diego State University

Assessment Consultant

Julie Weiss
*Curriculum and Assessment
Specialist
Elliot, Maine*

Music Consultant

Melanie Pinkert
*Music Faculty
Montgomery College, Maryland*

Cartographer

Mapping Specialists
Madison, Wisconsin

Internet Consultant

Amy George
Weston, Massachusetts

Diverse Needs Consultants

Erin Fry
Glendora, California

Colleen Guccione
Naperville, Illinois

Cathy Hix
*Swanson Middle School
Arlington, Virginia*

UNIT **1**

Europe During Medieval Times

Geography Challenge

Timeline Challenge

Medieval Europe, About 1300

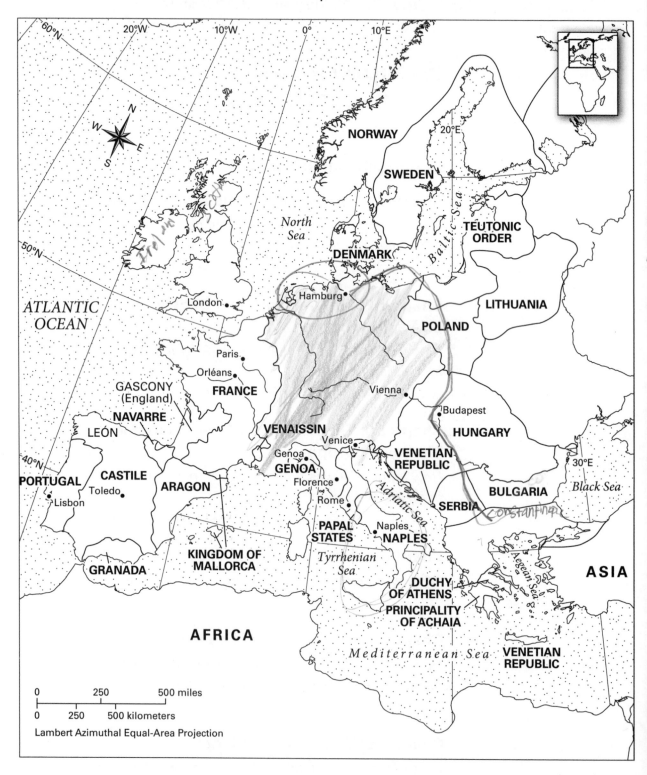

0   250   500 miles

0   250   500 kilometers

Lambert Azimuthal Equal-Area Projection

Geography Skills

Analyze the maps in "Setting the Stage" for Unit 1 in your book. Then answer the following questions and fill out the map as directed.

1. Locate the Holy Roman Empire and the Byzantine Empire. Label them on your outline map. What mountain range lies between these two empires?

2. Locate the Italian peninsula. Then locate the physical feature that separates it from the Holy Roman Empire. Draw and label this feature on your map.

3. Locate and label Constantinople.

4. Some parts of medieval Europe were actually islands. Locate and label these islands on your map.

5. The Byzantine Empire includes lands on which two continents?

6. Draw and label the Carpathian Mountains on your map. Through which medieval countries did they extend?

7. Label the Seine, Thames, Elbe, Tiber, and Danube rivers. List the cities that are located along these rivers. Why do you think large medieval cities were located along rivers?

8. Locate and circle the city of Hamburg on your map. What route might a trader from Constantinople have taken to reach the city of Hamburg?

Critical Thinking

Answer the following questions in complete sentences.

9. During medieval times, overland travel was dangerous, due to physical barriers, as well as wild animals and thieves. Because of this, sea travel was preferred. Based on what you know of the physical geography of Europe, why might its people have taken advantage of this form of transportation?

10. Suppose invaders from northern Africa and the Middle East attacked western Europe. What body of water would they have to cross to reach lands in western Europe?

11. The Roman Empire and the Holy Roman Empire are two different empires that existed at different times in history. The Roman Empire controlled all the land around the Mediterranean Sea, including present-day Spain, France, and England, and as far north as the Carpathian Mountains and the Black Sea. The Roman Empire ended around 476 C.E. The Holy Roman Empire, on the other hand, began around the year 800 C.E. How did the land areas controlled by the two empires differ?

The Legacy of the Roman Empire

To what extent have the contributions of ancient Rome influenced modern society?

PREVIEW

Part 1

Look at the map your teacher is projecting. On the map below, shade in the Roman Empire as it existed around 200 C.E. Then answer the questions below.

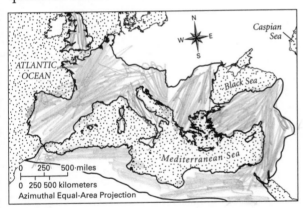

What do you notice about the Roman Empire around 200 C.E.? *They conquered many places. also on three*

What might be some disadvantages to controlling such a large empire?

There is too many people to control and you never know is they will turn on you

Part 2

Look at the second map your teacher is projecting. More than three hundred years have passed. On the map below, shade in the Roman Empire as it existed around 500 C.E. Then examine the differences between your two maps. Answer the questions below.

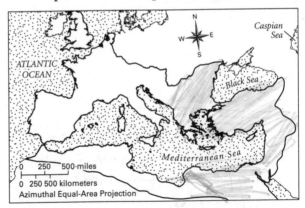

What do you notice about the second map compared to the first? *It is smaller*

What might have happened to cause these changes? *viking atccked rome*

How might Roman culture continue to influence these territories today? *math clock*

READING NOTES

Key Content Terms

As you complete the Reading Notes, use these terms in your answers.

Roman Empire	mosaic
empire	aqueduct
corruption	scribe
decline	proverb
Constantine	philosophy

Section 1.2

Read Section 1.2 and complete the following tasks.

1. Fill in the diagram by identifying and explaining examples of the different causes that led to the collapse of the Roman Empire.

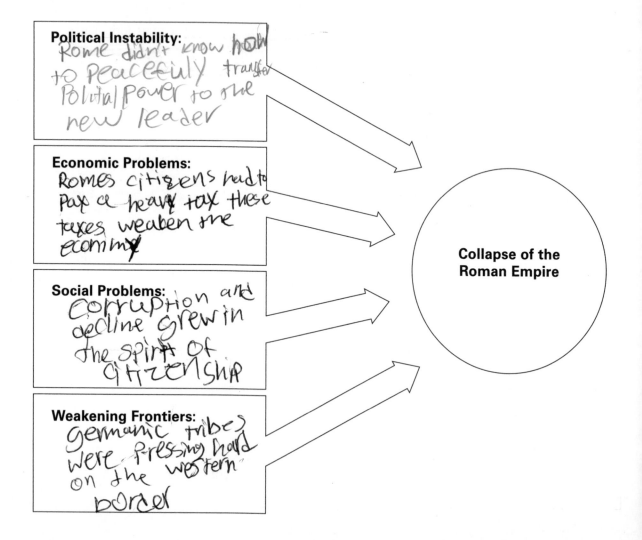

Political Instability: Rome didn't know how to peacefuly transfor Polital power to the new leader

Economic Problems: Romes citizens had to pax a heavy tax these texes weaben the ecomimy

Social Problems: corruption and decline grew in the spirit of citizenship

Weakening Frontiers: germanic tribes were pressing hard on the western border

Collapse of the Roman Empire

2. Complete the diagram to show the chain of events that led to the break-up
    of the Roman Empire and the rise of the Byzantine Empire.

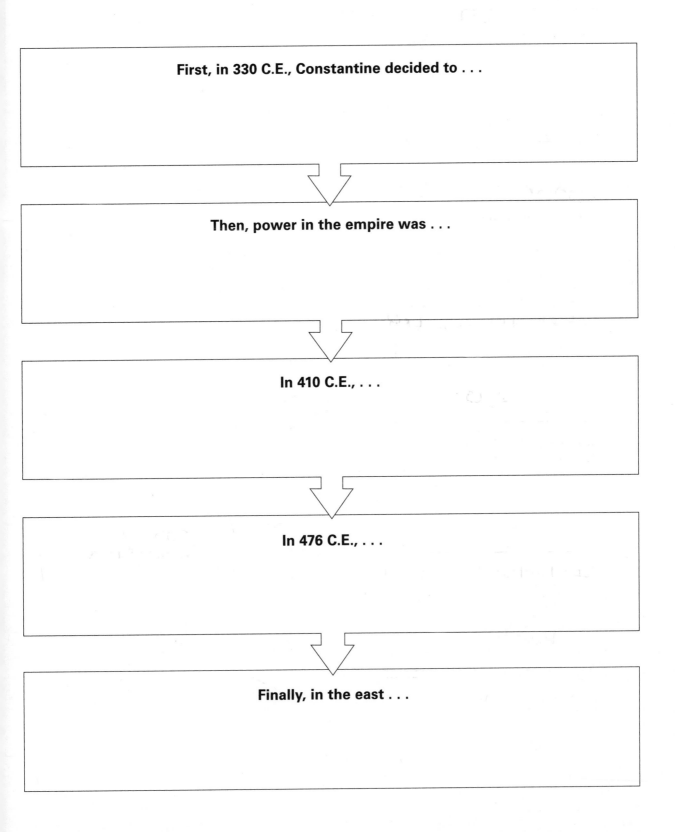

First, in 330 C.E., Constantine decided to . . .

Then, power in the empire was . . .

In 410 C.E., . . .

In 476 C.E., . . .

Finally, in the east . . .

If your class is doing the activity for this chapter, complete all questions in the following Reading Notes. *(Note: If your class is not doing the activity, skip Question 1 for each section.)*

Section 1.3

1. I think Modern Image ___D___ connects to Placard 1B because

   They are both Paintings

   I think Modern Image ___E___ connects to Placard 1D because

   they are both statues

2. List and describe at least three important art forms developed or made popular by the Romans.

   • *mosaics*
   • *statues*
   • *comeo*

3. What are two examples of Roman-influenced art in modern life? *Frescos, which you can sometimes see in resteraunt*

Section 1.4

1. I think Modern Image ___G___ connects to Placard 1C because

   used for transportation and made of cement

   I think Modern Image ___B___ connects to Placard 1H because

   they are both colsuem

2. List and describe at least three architectural features developed or made popular by the Romans.

   It is strait, a road and people use it
   • *Archs*
   • *vults*
   • *Domes*

3. What are two examples of Roman-influenced architecture in modern society, and what features of Roman architecture do they have?

4. List and describe two engineering achievements of the Romans.

Section 1.5

1. I think Modern Image _____ connects to Placard 1A because

   I think Modern Image __A__ connects to Placard 1F because
   They both track the day

2. Explain why Latin remains such an important language in the United States and around the world.

3. How were the numbers 1, 10, 100, and 1,000 written by the Romans?

Section 1.6

1. I think Modern Image __H__ connects to Placard 1E because

   I think Modern Image __C__ connects to Placard 1G because

2. Describe the philosophy of Stoicism.

3. What are some examples of Roman ideas about law and justice present in modern society?

4. How did the idea of citizenship descend from ancient Rome to modern times?

PROCESSING

Think of the different cultural influences from ancient Rome that you learned about in this chapter and how much they influence modern society. On the spectrum below, place the following Roman contributions where you think they most belong:

- Art (such as mosaics and murals)
- Architecture (such as domes and vaults)
- Engineering (such as aqueducts and roads)
- Latin language

- Roman numerals
- Roman courts and justice
- Citizenship

Roman numeral *roman courts and justice* *Arctecture* *Engeineering* *citizenship* *Latin* *Art*

Least Influence Today ————————————————— **Most Influence Today**

After you have placed the items on the spectrum, *on a separate sheet of paper,* write a paragraph in which you make an argument for the choice you made for "most influence today." Your paragraph should include:

- a topic sentence that clearly states your choice
- at least two specific examples of how your choice is evident in today's society
- a brief explanation of why some of the other contributions do not affect society as much
- a closing sentence that re-states your position

Make sure your paragraph is free of spelling and grammar errors.

The Development of Feudalism in Western Europe

How well did feudalism establish order in Europe in the Middle Ages?

In your own words, define *loyalty*. Then, in the scroll below, describe a situation, either from your own experience or from a news report, in which someone's loyalty was very important.

READING NOTES

Key Content Terms

As you complete the Reading Notes, use these terms in your answers.

Christianity	feudalism	serf
Charlemagne	fief	chivalry

Section 2.2

1. Create an obituary for Charlemagne. Remember that an *obituary* is an announcement of a person's death. It often includes a short biography and a summary of the person's accomplishments.

2. How did Charlemagne's relationship with the Catholic Church benefit both parties?

3. Why was there a need for order after the death of Charlemagne in 814?

In the downward pointing arrows on the diagram below, write an example of what each level of feudal society gave to the level below it. In the upward pointing arrows, write an example of what each level gave to the level above it.

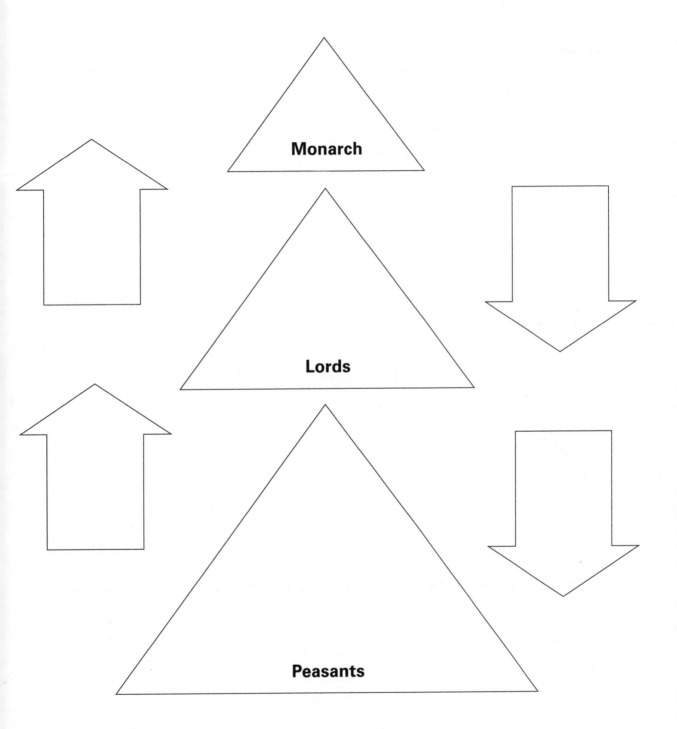

Section 2.4

1. Where did monarchs get their power?

Section 2.5

1. Sketch a typical manor house in medieval Europe. Be sure to include not only the house but its surroundings.

Section 2.6

1. Describe the three basic stages for a boy to become a knight.

2. What responsibilities did knights have in the feudal system?

Section 2.7

1. What were the responsibilities of peasants in the feudal system?

2. Why is William the Conqueror considered an important monarch?

2. What responsibilities did lords have in the feudal system?

3. What was the role of noblewomen in the feudal system?

3. Suppose that you are a knight. Write a code of chivalry for yourself. For example, your code might start, "I promise to be loyal to the Church and my lord."

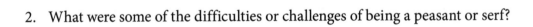

2. What were some of the difficulties or challenges of being a peasant or serf?

In the "report card" below, give feudalism a grade from A to F for each subject, based on how well you think it accomplished the goals listed. In the third column, provide a reason for your answer, making sure to include specific examples from your reading.

Subject	Grade	Reasons and Examples
Political Order Did feudalism create a stable form of government? Under feudalism, was Europe protected from outside threats?		
Economic Stability Did feudalism allow for the production and trade of essential goods?		
Prosperity Did feudalism foster wealth and well-being?		
Opportunity Under feudalism, were people able to better their circumstances through hard work or good fortune?		

The Roman Catholic Church in Medieval Europe

How influential was the Roman Catholic Church in medieval Europe?

PREVIEW

What is the most important building in your neighborhood or community? *On a separate sheet of paper,* make a simple sketch of the building. Next to your sketch, describe how the building is used.

READING NOTES

Key Content Terms

As you complete the Reading Notes, use these terms in your answers.

religion	Roman Catholic Church	sacrament	natural law
persecute	clergy	pilgrimage	religious order

Section 3.2

1. Which Roman Emperor issued a decree allowing Christians to practice their religion freely? How had Christians been treated by Romans before that time?

2. Describe two roles the Roman Catholic Church played in society after the fall of Rome.

   leadership and hospitality
   oroinized the food

---

3. Draw a diagram showing the hierarchy of the Roman Catholic Church during the High Middle Ages. For each group of clergy, write a one-sentence explanation of its role. Use the example below to begin your diagram, or create your own.

Pope
Supreme Head of the Roman Catholic Church

Cardinal　　**Cardinal**　　**Cardinal**

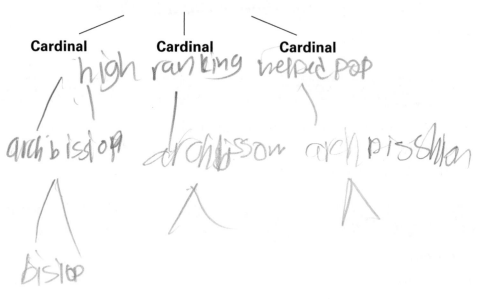

high ranking helped pop

archbishop   archdison   archbisshn

bislop

4. In your own words, summarize the conflict between Pope Gregory VII and the Holy Roman emperor, Henry IV. Use the words *appoint, duty, excommunicate, beg,* and *authority* in your summary.

bothe of them wanted to be charged of the

Section 3.3

1. According to the teachings of the Catholic Church, what was the purpose of sacraments?

2. Draw a simple symbol that illustrates the meaning of each of the seven sacraments.
    Then write one sentence explaining it.

Symbol	One-Sentence Explanation
Baptism	
Confirmation	
Eucharist	
Matrimony	
Holy Orders	
Penance	
Extreme Unction	

Section 3.4

1. Why did people undertake pilgrimages during the Middle Ages? What were some of the popular destinations of pilgrims?

   to show the respet to god

2. What were some of the challenges pilgrims faced on their journeys?

3. What was the goal of the Crusades?

   to retake jurusalim

Section 3.5

1. In what ways did the art of medieval Europe reflect the influence of the Roman Catholic Church?

2. Draw a simple sketch of each of the following key architectural features of cathedrals and define each one.

nave and transept	stained-glass window
gargoyle	flying buttress

1. Explain two advances in education during the Middle Ages.

University and using upper and lower case leter

2. Who was Thomas Aquinas? How did he bring together ancient philosophy and Christian theology?

3. Label the appropriate parts of the image at the right to help yourself remember the phrase, "bridging the gap between faith and reason." Use the terms *faith*, *reason*, and *Thomas Aquinas* in your labels.

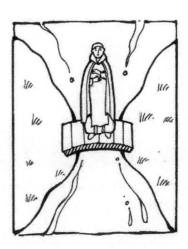

1. The word *holiday* comes from _____.
   What types of things did Christian holidays celebrate?

2. What were some of the ways in which people celebrated religious holidays?

Complete the matrix below to explain the similarities and differences between Benedictine monks and Franciscan friars.

	Benedictine Monks	Franciscan Friars
Where did they live?		
What promises or sacrifices did they make to join the order?		
How did they spend their time?		

PROCESSING

On a separate sheet of paper, create an acrostic poem that describes the influence of the Roman Catholic Church in medieval Europe.

Use your book, Reading Notes, and Student Handout 3 to complete your poem. Your poem must meet the following requirements.

- It must have nine short stanzas, or lines. Stanzas may vary in length; some may be only one line, while others may be longer.
- The first letter of the poem's stanzas must spell out the words THE CHURCH. So, the first word of Stanza 1 must begin with the letter *T,* the first word of Stanza 2 with the letter *H,* and so on. (Use the example at right to set up your poem).
- The poem must contain at least five of the Key Content Terms from this chapter.
- The poem must contain correct spelling and grammar. Type or write your final draft neatly in ink.

T

H

E

C

H

U

R

C

H

Life in Medieval Towns

What was life like in medieval European towns?

Look carefully at the image your teacher is projecting. This image of a marketplace in a European town during the 13th century includes clues about these three topics:

- living conditions
- job opportunities
- entertainment

1. In the image copy below, highlight at least one detail that gives a clue about each topic.

2. For each detail you highlight, add a note to the drawing that explains what you think that detail tells about the topic.

3. Draw a line connecting each detail to the matching note.

READING NOTES

Key Content Terms

As you complete the Reading Notes, use these terms in your answers.

charter   apprentice

guild   common law

Section 4.2

1. Where were towns in medieval Europe often located, and why?

    *They live around water
    and that makes it easier*

2. What contributed to the growth of towns in medieval Europe?

3. How was a town able to become independent of a feudal lord?

1. What were guilds? Why were they established?

2. How did guilds help their members and the families of their members?

3. Suppose that you have just been accepted as an apprentice to a stonemason. In the space below, write a short letter to a friend describing what this means for you and what the next few years will be like as you try to become a master stonemason and a member of the guild.

Section 4.4

1. How did trade change from the beginning of the Middle Ages to the High Middle Ages?

    Guilds were organization that oversaw the import and the export of goods

2. How did merchants become the most wealthy and powerful citizens of towns?

    Provided money and food

3. How were Jews often mistreated in medieval Europe? What opportunity was open to them?

Section 4.5

1. Describe the typical home in a medieval town.

2. What was difficult about growing up in a medieval town?

3. How were the lives of medieval girls different from those of modern girls?

Section 4.6

1. List at least three different conditions in medieval towns that led to the spread of disease.

2. What were some common diseases in medieval Europe?

3. What were some common practices or treatments used by medieval doctors?

Section 4.7

1. Describe two methods for deciding the guilt or innocence of accused criminals in the Early Middle Ages. They had to fight or go through a trial.

2. What were some ways in which criminals were punished in medieval Europe? Hanged or burned on a stake or put in a stock

3. What changes to the court system helped protect individual rights in the early 1100s in England? the system of royal court

1. What were some popular children's games in medieval Europe?

   Dolls, wooden Swords, balls

2. What were some leisure activities enjoyed by adults in medieval Europe?

   festivals and Plays

3. What was the difference between a mystery play and a miracle play?

   One is about religion and the other one isnt

PROCESSING

On a separate sheet of paper, create a daily diary page to describe what a typical day might have involved for someone living in a town in medieval Europe. Your page should include relevant details from the various aspects of life you learned about and include at least six entries. An example is shown, at right.

5:30 A.M. Rose from bed. Washed face with cold water. Plucked eyebrows. Tied hair in net and put on skirt and hat.

6:30 A.M. Ate breakfast (bread, cheese, weak cider). Threw scraps in street for hogs. Began walking to market.

7:30 A.M. Picked up shoes from cobblers' guild. Asked master if his hand is healing properly.

The Decline of Feudalism

How did events in Europe contribute to the decline of feudalism and the rise of democratic thought?

PREVIEW

On another sheet of paper, describe an event that you believe has changed the way you live, and explain how that event changed your life.

READING NOTES

Key Content Terms

As you complete the Reading Notes, use these terms in your answers.

Magna Carta	bubonic plague
habeas corpus	Hundred Years' War
Model Parliament	heretic

Section 5.2

1. What changes did Henry II make to the English legal system and how did these changes affect feudalism?

2. What changes did Magna Carta bring about in English government?

3. What was the Model Parliament, and why was it created?

4. In the Political Events box of the cause-and-effect diagram below, list examples of political developments in Europe that contributed to the decline of feudalism and the rise of democratic thought. (**Note:** You will be asked to return to this cause-and-effect diagram to complete it at different points in the Reading Notes.)

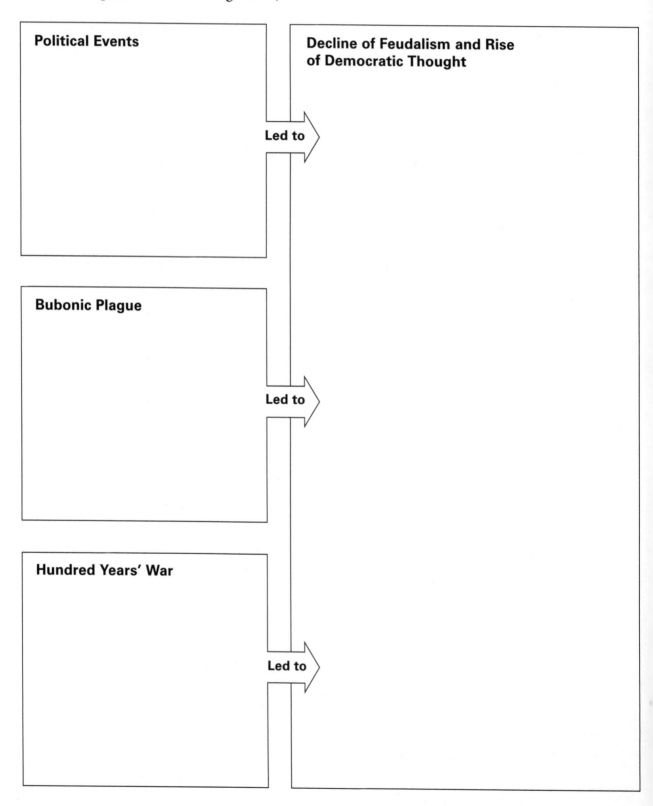

Political Events

Decline of Feudalism and Rise of Democratic Thought

Led to

Bubonic Plague

Led to

Hundred Years' War

Led to

1. Fill in the diagram below to illustrate the spread of the bubonic plague in the 14th century.

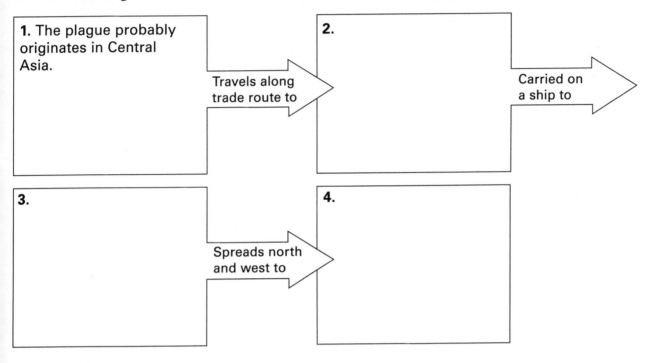

1. The plague probably originates in Central Asia.

Travels along trade route to

2.

Carried on a ship to

3.

Spreads north and west to

4.

On the map below, write the numbers from the boxes in the plague diagram in the correct locations to illustrate the spread of the bubonic plague.

The Spread of the Plague in the 14th Century

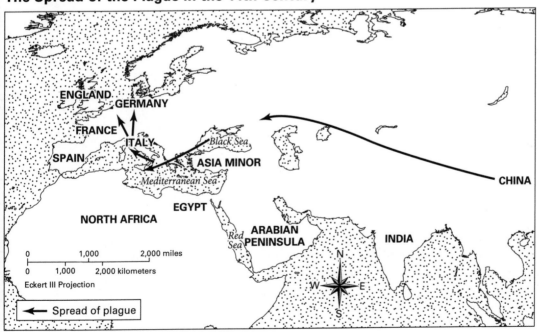

2. Why was the plague called the "Black Death"? What were some of the common symptoms?

3. How was the plague spread?

4. In the Bubonic Plague box of the cause-and-effect diagram, list examples of how the outbreak of the bubonic plague in Europe contributed to the decline of feudalism and the rise of democratic thought.

1. How did the Hundred Years' War start?

2. Why were the English able to defeat the French in early battles, such as the one at Crécy?

3. Who was Joan of Arc? What did she do for the French during the Hundred Years' War?

4. In the Hundred Years' War box of the cause-and-effect diagram, list examples of how the outbreak of war in Europe contributed to the decline of feudalism and the rise of democratic thought.

The figures below represent three individuals from medieval Europe—a noble, a commoner, and a knight. Draw facial features on each figure to express how he might have felt about events that led to feudalism's decline. Then, fill in each thought bubble by

- describing an event leading to the decline of feudalism from that person's perspective (include thoughts, feelings, and observations).
- explaining how the event affected that person's life.
- predicting how the decline of feudalism will affect that person's role in medieval society.

Check that your writing is free of misspellings and grammatical errors.

Noble

Commoner

Knight

Preparing to Write: Designing Interview Questions

During her lifetime, Joan of Arc became an international celebrity. People throughout Europe closely followed her military adventures and her trial.

Suppose that television had existed in Joan's time and that you are a television reporter interviewing her. Write interview questions to ask Joan of Arc about her accomplishments and attitudes. As you design your questions, you may refer to "The Trials of Joan of Arc" in your book.

What are three topics that you want to cover in your interview with Joan of Arc?

1.

2.

3.

Write three to five interview questions about the topics you have listed above. Be sure that your questions invite more than a "yes" or "no" answer. Also, be sure to write your questions directly to Joan of Arc.

Writing Interview Questions

Suppose you could interview a present-day celebrity you admire. Write
five interview questions you would ask this celebrity about his or her accomplishments. First, choose a celebrity. Be sure that your questions invite more than a
"yes" or "no" answer. Also, be sure to write your questions directly to the celebrity.

1.

2.

3.

4.

5.

Use this rubric to evaluate your interview questions. Make any changes
that you think will improve them.

Score	Description
3	All five interview questions focus on the celebrity's accomplishments, invite more than a "yes" or "no" answer, and address the celebrity directly.
2	Four interview questions focus on the celebrity's accomplishments, invite more than a "yes" or "no" answer, and address the celebrity directly.
I	Three interview questions focus on the celebrity's accomplishments, invite more than a "yes" or "no" answer, and address the celebrity directly.

The Byzantine Empire

How did the Byzantine Empire develop and form its own distinctive church?

PREVIEW

How do you think your experience exchanging paper tokens may be similar to trading goods in Constantinople? Examine the map your teacher is projecting. For each item in the first column of the chart, make an entry in the second column that connects your experience in the trading activity to history.

Historical Connection	Classroom Experience
• Traders came from various regions of the world, such as Africa, France, and China.	•
• Various goods were traded, such as ivory, wool, and silk.	•
• Many traders came to Constantinople to trade.	•
• Traders traveled to Constantinople by land and water routes.	•
• Traders brought new products back to their homelands after trading in Constantinople.	•

READING NOTES

Key Content Terms

As you complete the Reading Notes, use these terms in your answers.

Constantinople   Eastern Orthodox Church

Byzantine Empire   patriarch

Section 6.2

1. What about Constantinople's location made it an ideal capital of the Byzantine Empire?

2. Suppose that you are a trader visiting Constantinople for the first time. On the left side of the postcard below, write a few sentences to a friend back home describing what you see as you walk through the city's streets. On the right side, address your postcard to a friend in a faraway land selected from the map in this section of your book.

Section 6.3

1. What event forced Justinian I to start rebuilding parts of Constantinople?

2. What were some of the improvements made to Constantinople as a result of Justinian's public works projects?

3. Why was Justinian's Code significant?

1. Describe the relationship between religion and government in the Byzantine Empire.

2. For each image below, circle at least two details that illustrate aspects of Eastern Orthodox beliefs. Then, draw a line from each detail and explain how it was important to Eastern Orthodox faith.

In this altar icon, saints Cyril and Methodius hold a document with Cyrillic letters.

This is a Byzantine icon of Jesus. He is holding a Gospel.

Section 6.5

Three major disagreements contributed to a complete split in the Christian Church by 1054. Fill in the chart below with details of those three events and how they led to the final split.

Date	People Involved	Event That Led to the Disagreement	Result of the Disagreement
730 C.E.			
800 C.E.			
1054 C.E.			

PROCESSING

In the space below, create a real-estate advertisement to encourage people to move to Constantinople after the schism of 1054. Your advertisement must include the following elements:

- a memorable slogan
- a map that shows the location of Constantinople
- information about the city's geography, government, religion, and daily life
- four visuals that represent key ideas in the written information
- extra creative touches that make the advertisement look authentic
- writing that is free from spelling and grammatical errors

Timeline Skills

Analyze the Unit 1 timeline in your book. Also think about what you have learned in this unit. Then answer the following questions.

1. The Roman Empire included land in what three present-day continents?

2. What event led to the recognition of Christianity as the official religion of the Roman Empire?

3. The city of Constantinople was first known as what?

4. What event marks the beginning of the Middle Ages?

5. What new church developed in the Byzantine Empire?

6. For how many years did Justinian I rule the Byzantine Empire?

7. What did Charlemagne accomplish during his reign?

8. Why was Henry IV excommunicated?

9. How much longer than 100 years did the Hundred Years' War really last?

Critical Thinking

Use the timeline and the chapters in the unit to answer the following questions.

10. Describe three events that helped cause the fall of the Roman Empire.

11. Explain how Charlemagne's empire is an example of cooperation between the Church and European monarchs. Explain how the relationship between Gregory VII and Henry IV shows conflict between the Church and European monarchs.

12. Identify three events that eventually led to the decline of feudalism. Briefly explain how each weakened the feudal system.

13. If you could add three more events to this timeline, which would they be? List each event, and explain why you think it is important enough to add to the timeline.

   a.

   b.

   c.

Islam in Medieval Times

Geography Challenge

Chapter 7: The Origins and Spread of Islam

How did Islam originate and spread?

Chapter 8: Learning About World Religions: Islam

How do the beliefs and practices of Islam shape Muslims' lives?

Chapter 9: Muslim Innovations and Adaptations

What important innovations and adaptations did medieval Muslims make?

Chapter 10: From the Crusades to New Muslim Empires

How did the Crusades affect the lives of Christians, Muslims, and Jews?

Timeline Challenge

The Arabian Peninsula and Surrounding Lands

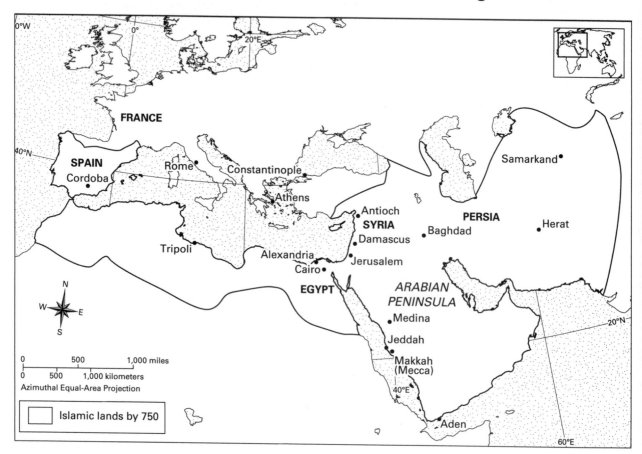

Islamic lands by 750

Azimuthal Equal-Area Projection

Geography Skills

Analyze the maps in "Setting the Stage" for Unit 2 in your book. Then answer the following questions and fill out the map as directed.

1. Locate the continents that surround the Arabian Peninsula and label them on your map.

2. Locate the body of water Arab traders crossed to reach Europe. Label this body of water.

3. Label the other oceans and seas on your map.

4. What cities on the Arabian Peninsula do you think would have been important trading centers? On your map, circle each one. Why do you think these cities became important trading centers?

5. How would the route of a trader traveling from Makkah to Cairo differ from that of a trader traveling from Makkah to Baghdad?

6. Lightly shade the areas on your map that were under Islamic rule by the year 750. After spreading along the northern coast of Africa, Muslim armies crossed the Strait of Gibraltar where Africa and Europe nearly meet. After conquering that peninsula, they were likely slowed by what physical feature?

7. According to the map, which city on the Arabian Peninsula is closest to Cairo? How do you think this might have affected the relationship between these two cities?

8. Locate the physical feature that formed the southern boundary of Islamic lands in Africa. Label this feature. Why do you think the empire stopped here?

Critical Thinking

Answer the following questions in complete sentences.

9. How might the location of the Arabian Peninsula have contributed to the rapid spread of Islam?

10. Based on what you have learned about the religion, economy, and physical geography of medieval Europe, why do you think the Muslims were not able to conquer most of that continent?

11. How did the location of the Arabian Peninsula help the Muslims conquer territory beyond the Arabian Peninsula?

The Origins and Spread of Islam

How did Islam originate and spread?

Muhammad began the religion of Islam in the 7th century. Look at the map showing the modern-day distribution of the followers of Islam, called Muslims. Then answer the following questions:

- Which pattern on the map represents the highest concentrations of Muslims? The lowest?

- In what regions of the world do the most Muslims live? The fewest?

- Based on this map, in what region of the world do you think the Islamic faith may have originated? Why?

Muslim Population, 2006

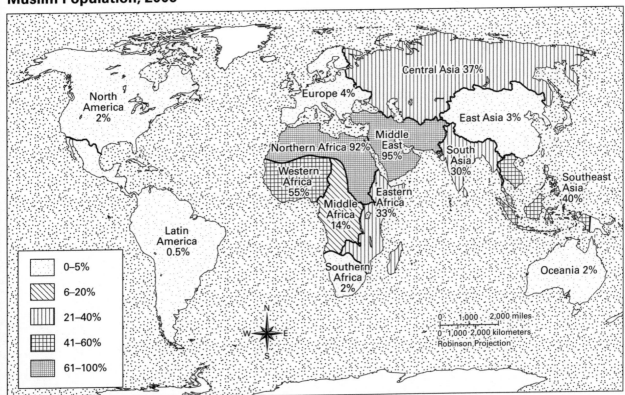

Key Content Terms

As you complete the Reading Notes, use these terms in your answers.

| Islam | polytheism | monotheism | boycott |
| Muhammad | prophet | Muslim | siege |

Section 7.2

1. Describe Makkah around the time of Muhammad's birth. Use the following terms and underline them in your description: *desert, prosperous, trading city, merchants, religious center.*

2. Why was the Ka'bah built, and how was it used at the time of Muhammad's birth?

3. Explain the ties that most Arabs shared during this time. Use the following terms and underline them in your explanation: *government, culture, language.*

If your class is doing the activity for this chapter, complete all the Reading Notes for each section. *(Note: If your class is not doing the activity, skip the first question of each section.)*

Section 7.3

1. Walk around the room to find the four words or terms that best match the part of the story you just heard. Write the English translations of the Arabic words here.

2. Write a four- to five-sentence summary of Muhammad's early life.

Section 7.4

1. Walk around the room to find the four words or terms that best match the part of the story you just heard. Write the English translations of the Arabic words here.

2. Where was Muhammad, and what was he doing, when the angel Gabriel told him, "You are the messenger of God"?

3. What does *Muslim* mean?

4. What is the holy book of Islam called? What does it contain?

Section 7.5

1. Walk around the room to find the four words or terms that best match the part of the story you just heard. Write the English translations of the Arabic words here.

2. What did Muhammad teach when he preached to the Makkans?

3. Why did Makkah's leaders try to prevent the spread of Muhammad's message?

4. Why is Jerusalem a holy city for Muslims?

Section 7.6

1. Walk around the room to find the four words or terms that best match the part of the story you just heard. Write the English translations of the Arabic words here.

2. On the timeline below, place each of the following events. Make sure you include the date for each event. One example is done for you.

    *   Muhammad and his followers leave on the hijrah.
    *   Muhammad develops a new Muslim community in Madinah.
    *   Fighting breaks out between the Muslims and Makkans.
    *   Makkans make a truce with the Muslims.
    *   Muhammad's army captures Makkah; he rededicates the Ka'bah to Allah.
    *   Muhammad delivers his Last Sermon.

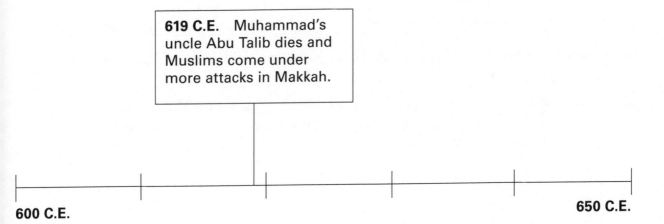

619 C.E. Muhammad's uncle Abu Talib dies and Muslims come under more attacks in Makkah.

600 C.E.

650 C.E.

Read Sections 7.7 and 7.8 and follow the directions below the map.

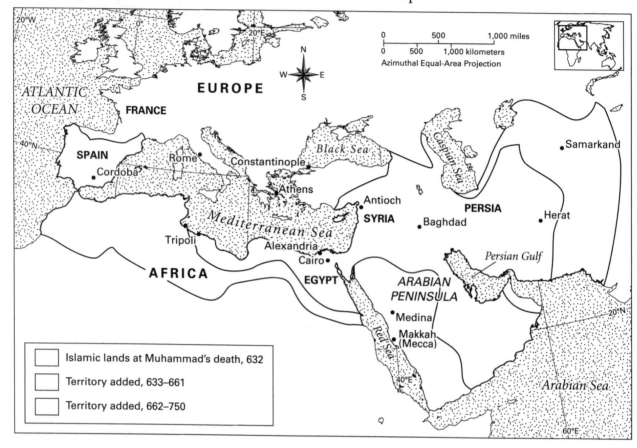

1. Complete the map by adding labels for Tours, Jerusalem, and Damascus. Then color in the key and the corresponding regions. Use three colors

2. Write a summary of the early spread of Islam. Include these events: Muhammad's death, the caliphs unify Arabia, Ali's election to the caliphate, the Muslim entry into Spain, and the Battle of Tours.

PROCESSING

Suppose that you are an Arab merchant living in the late 7th century. You have just traveled to Makkah and Madinah for business, and have met Muhammad and his followers. *On a separate sheet of paper,* write a short letter to a family member or a friend telling about your experience. In your letter, be sure to explain who Muhammad is and what he is teaching.

Learning About World Religions: Islam

How do the beliefs and practices of Islam shape Muslims' lives?

Carefully examine the images shown below. These images all relate to Islamic beliefs and practices. What questions do they raise? Write one question you would like answered about each image.

Question:

Question:

Question:

Question:

Question:

Chapter 8

READING NOTES

Key Content Terms

As you complete the Reading Notes, use these terms in your answers.

| Qur'an | Five Pillars of Islam | Ramadan | shari'ah |
| Sunnah | mosque | jihad | |

Section 8.2

Answer the following questions in complete sentences.

1. Where are Muslims found in the world today?

2. Complete the T-chart below by listing at least two ways in which Islam is similar
    to Judaism and Christianity and at least one way in which Islam is different from
    Judaism and Christianity.

Similarities	Differences

If your class is doing the activity for this chapter, read your assigned section of Chapter 8. Then answer the questions for that section. You will take notes for the other sections during the class presentations. *(Note: If your class is not doing the activity, complete the Reading Notes after you read each section.)*

Section 8.3

1. What is the difference between the Qur'an and the Sunnah?

2. How are hadith related to the Sunnah?

3. How are the Qur'an and the Sunnah related to the Five Pillars of Islam?

Section 8.4

1. Explain the meaning of the two parts of the Muslim shahadah.

   "There is no god but God…"   "…and Muhammad is the messenger of God"

2. According to Muslims, who is Allah?

3. What do Muslims believe about angels and about judgment?

Section 8.5

1. What is salat and what purpose does it serve?

2. Where and how often do Muslims pray?

3. Describe at least three of the rituals Muslims practice in their daily prayers.

Section 8.6

1. What is zakat and why do Muslims practice it?

2. How much of their surplus wealth are Muslims expected to give to charity?

3. What kinds of things does zakat pay for?

Section 8.7

1. What is siyam and when is it performed?

2. What rule about food do Muslims observe during Ramadan?

3. What does Ramadan encourage and teach?

Section 8.8

1. What is the hajj and what values does it promote?

2. What do Muslims do during the hajj?

3. What important sites do Muslims visit during the hajj?

Section 8.9

1. In your own words, explain the meaning of jihad.

2. What does the Qur'an tell Muslims to do regarding jihad, and how was this form of jihad interpreted by early Muslims?

3. How does jihad relate to Muslims and their personal struggles?

Section 8.10

1. What is shari'ah, and how did it develop?

2. How does shari'ah guide Muslim life?

3. How has shari'ah changed over time?

PROCESSING

For each of the eight sections of the star below, write a one-sentence explanation of that belief or practice of Islam. Then create one simple symbol or illustration to help explain it. Place your explanations and illustrations in or next to the appropriate section of the star.

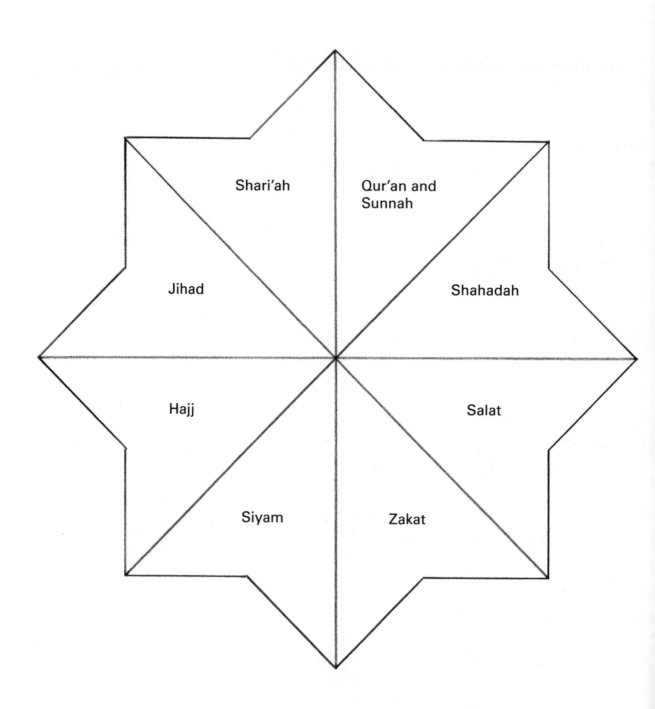

Muslim Innovations and Adaptations

What important innovations and adaptations did medieval Muslims make?

Think of some ways in which your life is influenced by cultures in other parts of the world. Consider such things as food, language, holidays, and music. Fill in the spoke diagram below by doing the following in each box:

- Draw a simple symbol that represents a way in which your life is influenced by cultures from other parts of the world.

- Write a short explanation of the influence.

- If possible, include the country of origin.

Then, list any ways that particular food, language, holiday, or music has been adapted, or changed, since coming to your community.

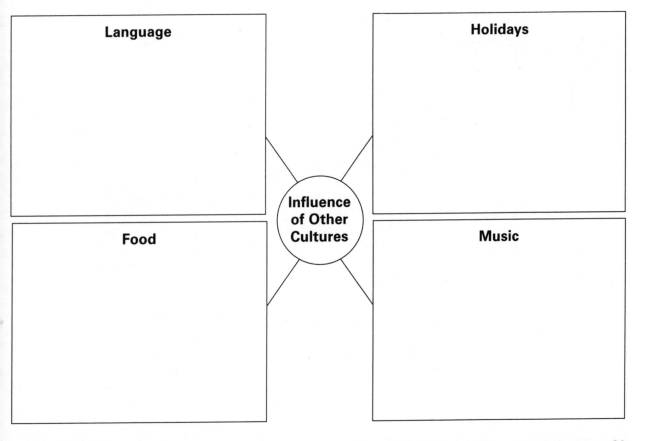

READING NOTES

Key Content Terms

As you complete the Reading Notes, use these terms in your answers.

adaptation   cultural diffusion   immortal

innovation   philosopher   evolution

Section 9.2

1. Why did Islamic culture flourish, despite the fact that the Muslim empire did not last?

2. What is *cultural diffusion?*

3. Look at the map of medieval trade routes, below. How did the location of Islamic lands make cultural diffusion possible?

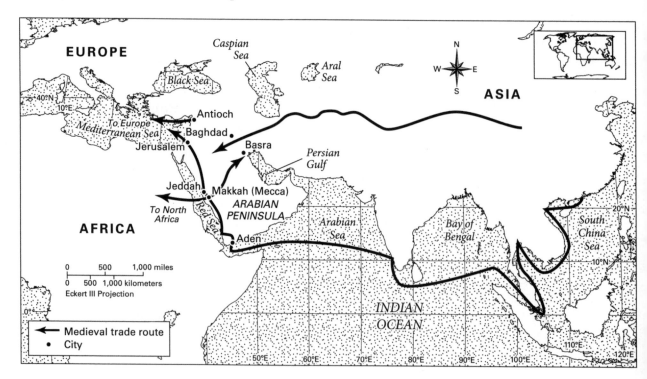

4. How did trade help to spread and connect ideas from different cultures? List at least two ideas that may have traveled along the trade routes on the map.

If your class is doing the activity for this chapter, complete all the Reading Notes for each section. *(Note: If your class is not doing the activity, skip the first question of each section.)*

As you visit each station, determine the section of your book that corresponds with what is shown on the placard. Write the placard letter in Question 1 for that section and give details that show how it relates to the section category. Then complete the remaining Reading Notes.

Section 9.3: City Building and Architecture

1. Record two details from Placard _____ that show how it relates to this category.

2. List three important details about the city of Baghdad.

3. Describe how mosques are designed.

Section 9.4: Scholarship and Learning

1. Record two details from Placard _____ that show how it relates to this category.

2. What factors combined to promote learning in Muslim lands?

3. How did Muslim philosophers follow the example of Greek scholars?

Section 9.5: Science and Technology

1. Record two details from Placard _____ that show how it relates to this category.

2. Describe two contributions made by Muslim scholars in these two categories.

Zoology	Astronomy
•	•
•	•

3. What technological advancements did Muslims make to take advantage of scarce water resources?

Section 9.6: Geography and Navigation

1. Record two details from Placard _____ that show how it relates to this category.

2. List two accomplishments of Muslims in this category.

3. Describe the purpose of the two navigational instruments adapted and perfected by Muslims.

Section 9.7: Mathematics

1. Record two details from Placard _____ that show how it relates to this category.

2. What are two reasons why al-Khwarizmi's books were important to the field of mathematics?

3. Why is the Indian concept of zero, which Muslims helped spread, significant?

Section 9.8: Medicine

1. Record two details from Placard _____ that show how it relates to this category.

2. In the chart, list one example of Muslim contributions in each area of medicine:

Hospitals	Medication	Surgery	Disease

3. What role did Ibn Sina's book, *The Canon of Medicine,* play in the medieval world?

Section 9.9: Bookmaking and Literature

1. Record two details from Placard _____ that show how it relates to this category.

2. List two ways Muslims adapted and expanded bookmaking.

3. List one example of famous Muslim literature. Where did these stories originate, and where did they spread?

Section 9.10: Art and Music

1. Record two details from Placard _____ that show how it relates to this category.

2. What types of designs did Muslims use in their decorative art?

3. List two ways textiles were important to medieval Muslims.

4. What was unique about the music that developed in Cordoba, Spain?

Section 9.11: Recreation

1. Record one detail from Placard _____ that shows how it relates to this category.

2. For each of the favorite pastimes below, write one sentence explaining what the pastime involves and another sentence explaining why it became popular with medieval Muslims.

Polo	Chess
•	•
•	•

PROCESSING

Copy a larger, horizontal version of spectrum below onto another sheet of paper. Examine your completed Reading Notes. Then choose five Muslim adaptations or innovations to place along your spectrum. For each adaptation or innovation:

- Label the adaptation or innovation on the appropriate place on your spectrum, based on how significant you think it was.

- Draw an appropriate symbol or illustration near the label.

- Write one sentence explaining your placement of the adaptation or innovation on the spectrum.

←——→

Least significant
adaptation or innovation

Most significant
adaptation or innovation

Preparing to Write: Listing Descriptive Words

You have just read about some of the many foods enjoyed by early Muslims. You also read about the exchange of foods between the Middle East and other parts of the world through cultural diffusion. What do you think these foods are like? Have you eaten any of them before? Complete the chart below by listing descriptive words, or adjectives, that tell how six of these foods might smell, look, and taste. An example is provided for you.

Food	How It Might Look	How It Might Smell	How It Might Taste
plantain	lumpy	sweet	delicious

Writing a Descriptive Paragraph

Suppose that you are a guest at the court of Caliph Ma'mun in medieval Baghdad. Ibrahim ibn al-Mahdi has prepared a great feast during your visit. Using your list of descriptive words and others you might think of, write an account of the feast as if you were telling a friend about it. Be sure to identify the foods you ate, describe what they were like, and add any other details you might know about them.

Use this rubric to evaluate your account. Make changes to your account if you need to.

Score	Description
3	The account presents a clear account with many descriptive words and details. The account is well constructed, with a topic sentence, supporting details, and a conclusion. There are no spelling or grammar errors.
2	The account presents a clear account and has some descriptive words and details. The account has a topic sentence, supporting details, and a conclusion. There are some spelling or grammar errors.
1	The account does not present a clear account and has few descriptive words and details. It lacks a topic sentence, supporting details, and a conclusion. There are many spelling or grammar errors.

From the Crusades to New Muslim Empires

How did the Crusades affect the lives of Christians, Muslims, and Jews?

PREVIEW

As your class analyzes the image of the map your teacher is projecting, record responses to the questions below.

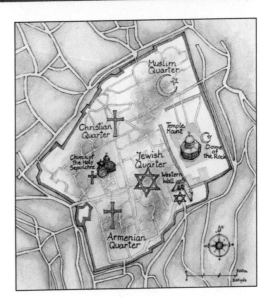

1. How is the area on the map divided?

2. What religions are represented in the different quarters?

3. What important landmarks do you see? With which religion is each affiliated?

4. What do you think makes this an important or special city?

5. Why might people fight over this city?

READING NOTES

Key Content Terms

As you complete the Reading Notes, use these terms in your answers.

Crusades	Inquisition	shah
sultan	anti-Semitism	
Holy Land	segregation	

Section 10.2

1. After reading Section 10.2, list below at least three causes of the Crusades.

    •

    •

    •

2. List one reason why Jerusalem is holy to Christians.

3. List one reason why Jerusalem is holy to Muslims.

4. List one reason why Jerusalem is holy to Jews.

Section 10.3

Complete the flow chart below by writing a brief summary of the main phases of the Crusades. Within each phase are a list of key terms to include in your summary.

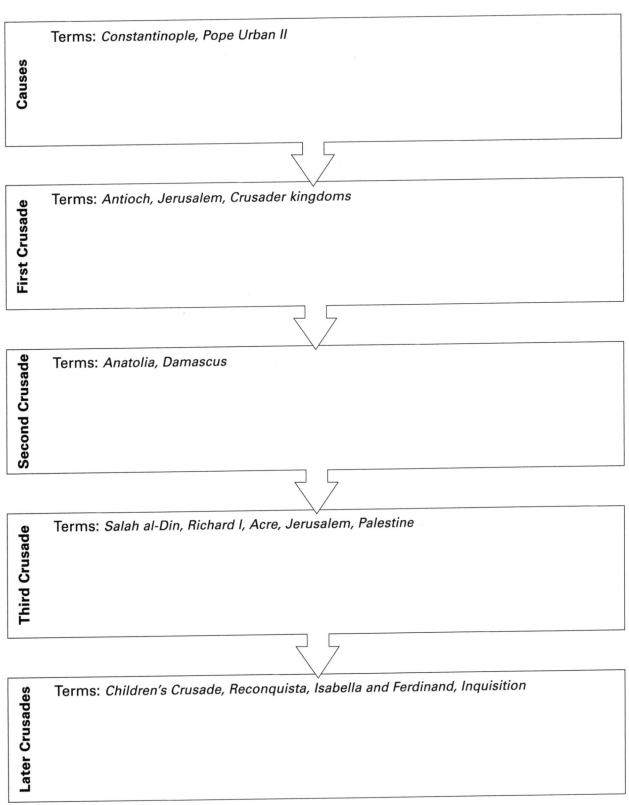

Causes

Terms: *Constantinople, Pope Urban II*

First Crusade

Terms: *Antioch, Jerusalem, Crusader kingdoms*

Second Crusade

Terms: *Anatolia, Damascus*

Third Crusade

Terms: *Salah al-Din, Richard I, Acre, Jerusalem, Palestine*

Later Crusades

Terms: *Children's Crusade, Reconquista, Isabella and Ferdinand, Inquisition*

Complete the T-charts below by listing the positive and negative impacts of the Crusades on Christians and Muslims and the negative impacts on Jews.

Impact of the Crusades on Christians

Positive	Negative

Impact of the Crusades on Muslims

Positive	Negative

Impact of the Crusades on Jews

Negative	

Section 10.7

1. Who were the Mongols, and what did they do under their leader Genghis Khan and his successors?

2. How did the Mongol empire change after converting to Islam?

3. What led to the decline of the Mongol Empire?

Section 10.8

Write a two- or three-sentence description of each Muslim empire on the map. Consider including its location, religious affiliation, leadership style, and effects of its rule on non-Muslims or other empires.

Major Muslim Empires, 900–1500

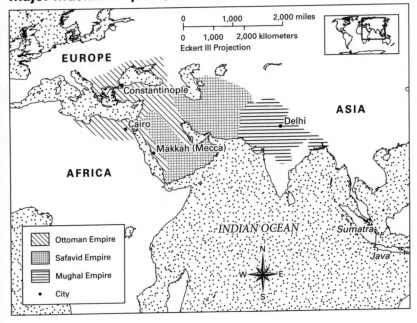

Ottoman Empire

Safavid Empire

Mughal Empire

PROCESSING

Suppose that you are a medieval journalist who has been given an opportunity to interview three people—a Muslim, a Jew, and a Christian—to learn more about how each was affected by the Crusades.

If necessary, on a separate sheet of paper, write three interview questions that you would ask these people. Make sure that each question can be answered by all three people. Then write a response to the question from each person's perspective. You might set up your interview as shown below. You may use the sample question in your interview.

Question 1:   In your opinion, what caused the Crusades?

Question 2:

Question 3:

Muslim

Response to Question 1:

Response to Question 2:

Response to Question 3:

Jew

Response to Question 1:

Response to Question 2:

Response to Question 3:

Christian

Response to Question 1:

Response to Question 2:

Response to Question 3:

Timeline Skills

Analyze the Unit 2 timeline in your book. Also think about what you have learned in this unit. Then answer the following questions.

1. According to Islamic teachings, what significant event happened to Muhammad in about 610 C.E.?

2. How many years did Muhammad preach his new religion in Makkah before he moved to Madinah?

3. Why did Muhammad and his followers move to Madinah?

4. What two things did Muhammad do shortly before his death?

5. To what lands did Islam expand in the 120 years after Muhammad's death?

6. When was an official version of the Qur'an created, and what was its impact?

7. What happened to Islamic civilization from 750 to 1250?

8. How long did the Crusades last?

9. Why did Christians launch the Crusades?

10. What was the purpose of the Spanish Inquisition?

Critical Thinking

Use the timeline and the chapters in the unit to answer the following questions.

11. What group—Christians, Muslims, or Jews—gained the most from the Crusades? Which group lost the most? Why?

12. Which Muslim innovation or adaptation do you think was most significant, and why?

13. If you could add three more events to this timeline, which would they be? List each event, and explain why you think it is important enough to add to the timeline.

    a.

    b.

    c.

UNIT **3**

The Culture and Kingdoms of West Africa

Geography Challenge

Chapter 11: Early Societies in West Africa

What was the most significant factor in the development of early societies in West Africa?

Chapter 12: Ghana: A West African Trading Empire

To what extent did trans-Saharan trade lead to Ghana's wealth and success?

Chapter 13: The Influence of Islam on West Africa

In what ways did Islam influence West African society?

Chapter 14: The Cultural Legacy of West Africa

In what ways do the cultural achievements of West Africa influence our culture today?

Timeline Challenge

Africa

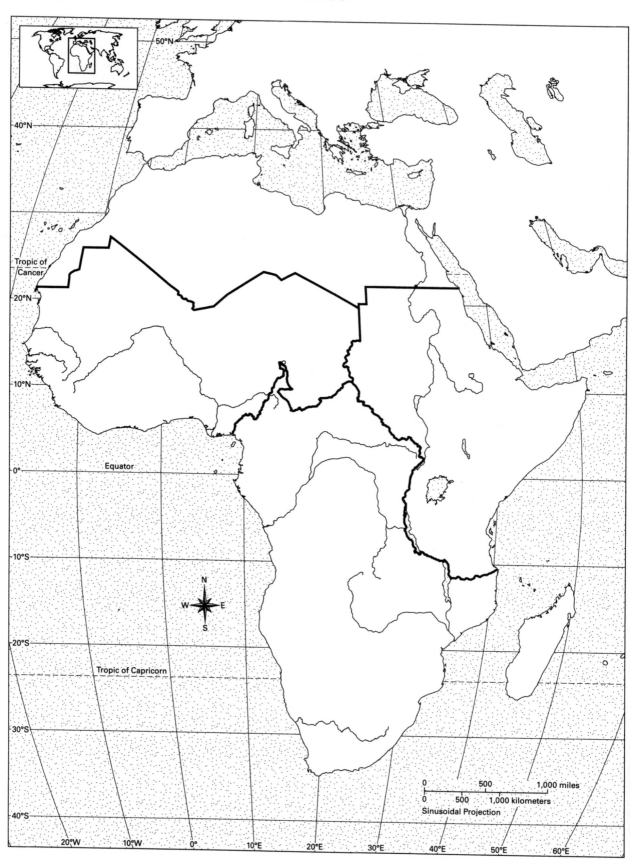

Geography Skills

Analyze the maps in "Setting the Stage" for Unit 3 in your book. Then answer the following questions and fill out the map as directed.

1. Locate the ocean that borders Africa on the west. Label it on your map. Then, locate and label the ocean that borders Africa on the east. Next, locate and label the sea that borders Africa on the north.

2. Locate the four regions of the continent of Africa. Label these regions on your map.

3. Locate the Sahara and the Sahel. Label them on your map.

4. Look at the map of Africa's vegetation zones in your book. In which of these zones do you think people were least likely to settle? Why?

5. In what region of Africa were the kingdoms of Ghana, Mali, and Songhai located? What vegetation zones are found in this part of Africa?

6. Label the Niger and Senegal rivers. Through which two kingdoms did the Niger River extend?

7. Which of the three West African kingdoms was the largest?

8. Locate the city of Timbuktu on your map. Label it. On what river is it located?

9. Timbuktu was part of which two West African kingdoms?

Critical Thinking

Answer the following questions in complete sentences.

10. Why do you think the Niger and Senegal rivers were important to the civilizations that developed in West Africa?

11. Islam spread into West Africa beginning in the 700s. What part of Africa do you think was first introduced to this religion? Along what route do you think Islam traveled from that starting point into West Africa?

Early Societies in West Africa

What was the most significant factor in the development of early societies in West Africa?

Look at the images your teacher is projecting. They are also shown below.

The Savanna

The Forest

Climate: The savanna has hot, dry winters and warm, wet summers. The year-round temperatures remain warm, ranging from 70°F to 100°F.

Vegetation: At places where there is more rainfall, there are trees and grasses. In the drier spots, bushes replace trees.

Climate: The forest is wetter than the savanna and gets rainfall year-round. Temperatures vary greatly between the summer and the winter months.

Vegetation: Many trees and shrubs grow here, such as oil palms, yams, and kola trees.

In which environment do you think a city was most likely to develop? Give two reasons for your answer.

READING NOTES

Key Content Terms

As you complete the Reading Notes, use these terms in your answers.

Sahara	Niger River	smelting
Sahel	Nok	Jenne-jeno
savanna	artifact	tribute

Section 11.2

1. Below is an outline map of West Africa. Label the Sahara, the Sahel, the savanna, and the forest. Then draw and label the types of vegetation found in each area. Also label the Niger River. You can use the maps in the Setting the Stage feature at the beginning of this unit to help you.

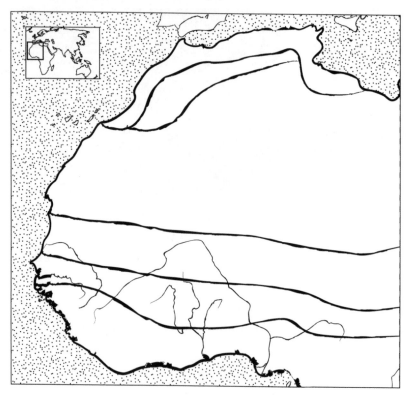

2. How did geography affect trade in West Africa?

Suppose that you are going to write and illustrate a story for third graders that explains why early societies developed in West Africa. Use the storyboard below to create your story by following the directions in each section's Reading Notes.

Panel 1	Panel 2

Panel 3	Panel 4

Section 11.3

1. In Panel 1 of your storyboard, create a drawing and caption that describe the earliest communities in West Africa.

2. In Panel 2 of your storyboard, create a drawing and caption that describe how and why villages formed from these early communities. Be sure to include the reasons why family-based communities joined together to form villages.

Section 11.4

1. In Panel 3 of your storyboard, create a drawing and caption that describe how and why some villages became trading sites and eventually grew into larger towns and cities.

2. Describe the process of smelting used by the Nok to make iron tools.

3. How did the ability to make iron tools affect food production and the types of jobs that villagers performed in West Africa?

4. How did the location of Jenne-jeno cause it to become a large, busy city?

Section 11.5

1. In Panel 4 of your storyboard, create a drawing and caption that describe how and why some of the wealthiest cities were able to conquer more territory and become a kingdom.

2. What is *tribute?* What did it mean when a conquered group paid tribute?

3. List at least one advantage and one disadvantage of being part of a kingdom.

Advantage	Disadvantage

PROCESSING

Several factors led to the development of early societies and kingdoms in West Africa. These factors include geography, the spread of ironworking, the specialization of labor, and increased local trade. Which of these factors do you think was most important to the development of a settlement into a city and, later, a kingdom?

In the space below, write a paragraph in which you argue what factor you think was most significant in the development of early societies in West Africa. Your paragraph should include:

- a topic sentence that clearly states your choice
- at least two specific examples that show how your choice was important
- a closing sentence that restates your position

Make sure that your paragraph is free of spelling and grammatical errors.

Ghana: A West African Trading Empire

To what extent did trans-Saharan trade lead to Ghana's wealth and success?

PREVIEW

You are traveling to Ghana with a few cattle to trade. In the "Original Rank" column in the chart below, rank the trade items by placing a "1" next to the item you would most want to trade for. Rank the other items based on how much you would want to trade for them until you place a "5" next to the item you would least want to trade for.

Trade Items	Original Rank	Scenario 1 Rank	Scenario 2 Rank
two ounces of gold			
one pound of salt			
a bundle of wool			
several hides of leather			
two sacks of grain			

What factor or factors did you consider as you ranked these items?

Your teacher will give you Scenario 1. Write it in the space below. Then rank the items again, based on this scenario. Did your rankings change? Why or why not?

Now your teacher will give you Scenario 2. Write it in the space below. Then rank the items again, based on this scenario. Did your rankings change again? Why or why not?

READING NOTES

Key Content Terms

As you complete the Reading Notes, use these terms in your answers.

Ghana

matrilineal

trans-Saharan trade

Section 12.2

1. Write three statements to describe Ghana's king.

   a.

   b.

   c.

2. What two groups helped the king govern? How?

3. Who would inherit the throne after a king died? Why?

Section 12.3

1. Around the camel, draw or list three products a North African trader might bring to trade in West Africa. Around the Wangaran's basket, draw or list three products the people of the southern forest areas might bring to trade with the North African traders.

2. Why was travel across the Sahara challenging?

3. What two factors led to the growth of trans-Saharan trade?

Section 12.4

1. Fill in the chart below with details about the gold-salt trade in West Africa.

	Gold	Salt
Why it was valuable to West Africans		
Where it came from		

2. How did the gold-salt trade benefit Ghana?

1. Fill in the speech bubbles for the Wangaran gold miner and the North African trader. Have each explain what he does during silent bartering.

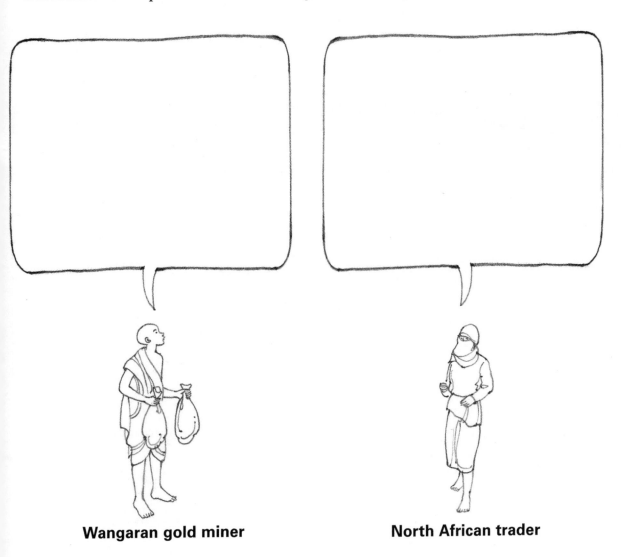

Wangaran gold miner　　　　　**North African trader**

2. What were two advantages of the silent-barter system?

List and describe two reasons why the kingdom of Ghana declined.

PROCESSING

In the speech bubble for each figure below, write two sentences that the figure might say. The sentences should explain how that figure benefited from trans-Saharan trade.

North African trader

Wangaran gold miner

King of Ghana

The Influence of Islam on West Africa

In what ways did Islam influence West African society?

Examine the image below. Think about what you may already know about Islamic influences. Circle any of the categories listed below for which you see examples of Islamic influences in the image.

Categories of Influences

Religious Practices	Government/Law	Education
Language	Architecture	Decorative Arts

Now annotate the image by circling each example of Islamic influence. Draw a line from your circle to the space next to the image. Then write a sentence there explaining why you believe this is an example of an Islamic influence.

READING NOTES

Key Content Terms

As you complete the Reading Notes, use these terms in your answers.

Mali   patrilineal

Mansa Masu   textile

Songhai

Section 13.2

Read this section. Then, on the timeline below, place four dates that you believe were significant to the spread of Islam in West Africa. For each entry, write a short caption that explains why that date was important to the spread of Islam.

| 1000 | 1100 | 1200 | 1300 | 1400 | 1500 |

If you are doing the activity, do all three parts. *(Note: If you are not doing the activity, skip Step 1 for each chart.)*

Read one of Sections 13.3 to 13.8, and analyze the posted photographs for examples of that influence of Islam on West Africa. Then follow these steps to fill in the charts below.

Step 1   Write the letter of each photograph that shows an example of the influence of Islam on West Africa and a brief explanation of that example. (An example is given below.)

Step 2   Answer the questions in the second column from your reading of that section.

Step 3   Make a simple illustration of something you think best represents that influence of Islam on West Africa.

Section 13.3 Influence of Islam on Religious Practices

Letter of Placard and Explanation	Questions for this Section	Simple Illustration
D *shows a mosque with minarets*	List two ways that West Africans adopted Islamic religious practices. List two examples of how they preserved their own religious practices.	

Section 13.4 Influence of Islam on Government and Law

Letter of Placard and Explanation	Questions for this Section	Simple Illustration
	How did the line of succession change with the arrival of Islam? How did the structure of government change under Islamic influence? Give one example of how shari'ah was different from customary law.	

Section 13.5 Influence of Islam on Education

Letter of Placard and Explanation	Questions for This Section	Simple Illustration
	List three ways that the Islamic love of learning influenced West Africa.	

Section 13.6 Influence of Islam on Language

Letter of Placard and Explanation	Questions for This Section	Simple Illustration
	Though West Africans still used their native language in everyday speech, in what aspects of society did Arabic become the primary language? How did the use of Arabic in West Africa become an important tool for historians?	

Section 13.7 Influence of Islam on Architectural Styles		
Letter of Placard and Explanation	Questions for This Section	Simple Illustration
	What two new architectural changes were influenced by Islam? How were the homes built by al-Saheli different from traditional West African houses?	

Section 13.8 Influence of Islam on Decorative Arts		
Letter of Placard and Explanation	Questions for This Section	Simple Illustration
	List and describe two new decorative arts or styles that West Africans adopted from Muslims. How did West African clothing change with the arrival of Islam?	

PROCESSING

Use the figure of the West African below to create a sensory figure by showing what he sees, hears, feels, tastes, or smells. Follow these steps:

1. In each box, your sensory sentence will begin "With my _____, I ..." You must complete the sentence by describing a concrete example of an Islamic influence in West Africa. Refer to any of the five senses in your sentences.

2. Each sensory sentence should relate to a different one of the six topics you studied—religious practices, government and law, education, language, architectural styles, and decorative arts. For example, "With my ears, I hear Muslims in West Africa being called to prayer five times each day."

With my _____, I

With my ears, I hear Muslims in West Africa being called to prayer five times each day.

With my _____, I

With my _____, I

With my _____, I

CHAPTER 14

The Cultural Legacy of West Africa

In what ways do the cultural achievements of West Africa influence our culture today?

When your teacher directs you, practice reciting in unison the appropriate call or response in the first verse of the song "Everybody Ought to Know."

"Everybody Ought to Know"

Call: Everybody ought to know

Response: Everybody ought to know

Call: Everybody ought to know

Response: Everybody ought to know

Together: Everybody ought to know

Call: What freedom is

Response: What freedom is

For verses 2–5, replace *freedom* with *justice, friendship, happiness,* and then repeat *freedom.*

After your perform the call-and-response song, answer the following questions.

1. How did it feel to sing this call-and-response song?

2. What do you think is the purpose of this song?

3. Do you think that the call-and-response tradition has influenced modern music? If so, how?

READING NOTES

Key Content Terms

As you complete the Reading Notes, use these terms in your answers.

oral tradition	call and response
griot	terra-cotta
genealogy	appliqué
folktale	kente

Section 14.2

1. Why has oral tradition been so important in West Africa?

2. What are *griots?* Why were they important in West African culture?

3. How have West African folktales become a part of the culture in the Americas?

4. How do West African written and oral traditions influence life today?

1. What functions did music serve in medieval West Africa?

2. Describe call-and-response singing.

3. Label each of the following traditional West African instruments by matching their descriptions in your book with the pictures.

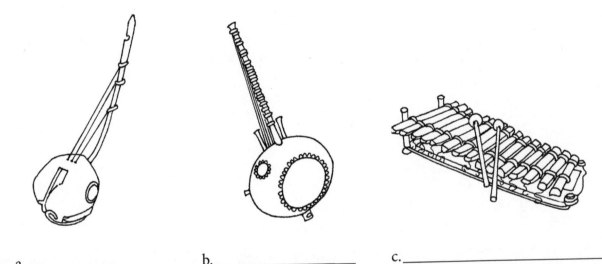

a. _____   b. _____   c. _____

4. How does West African music and dance influence music today?

Section 14.4

1. What functions did visual art serve in West Africa?

2. What forms of visual art did West Africans create?

3. How has West African visual art influenced modern art and culture?

PROCESSING

You have been asked by a museum curator to create a small display featuring cultural achievements of West Africa. Choose three specific examples of cultural achievements to highlight in your display. You must choose one that is a written or oral tradition, one that relates to music, and one that is an example of a visual art.

For each of your display items, do the following *on a separate sheet of paper.*

- Draw a representation of your cultural achievement or find an image or drawing on the Internet that you can print out and attach.

- Label your achievement and give a short description of what it was and how it was important to medieval West African culture.

- Discuss how that achievement has influenced modern society.

Preparing to Write: Identifying Supporting Details

Modern-day griot Youssou N'Dour tells stories in his songs that praise traditions and teach lessons. If you were a griot, what would you sing about? For example, you might sing about a yearly festival, a holiday, a family tradition, or even an annual sporting event. Choose a tradition or life lesson that matters to you. Write it in the center oval of the word web below. Then complete the web by adding supporting details that tell about this topic. Include interesting and descriptive words, and add as many items to the word web as you need.

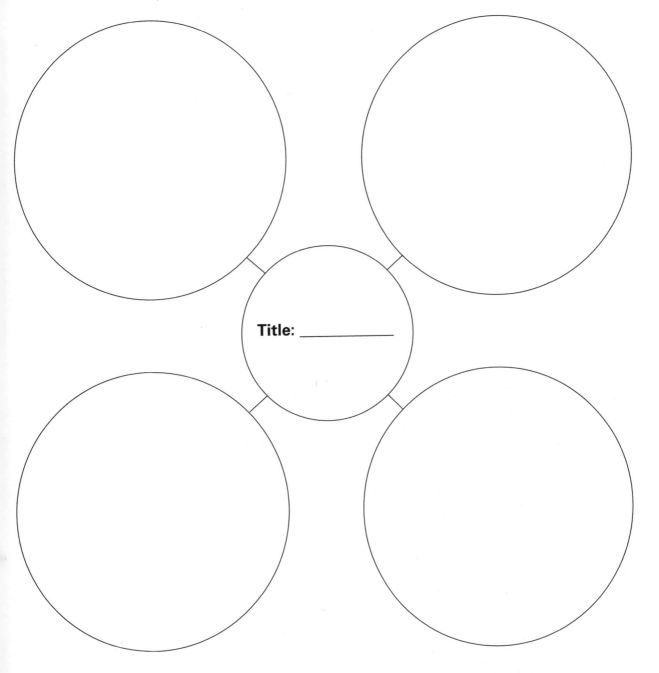

Title: _____

Writing Lyrics for a Griot Song

Suppose that you are a griot, like Youssou N'Dour. Use the details you recorded in the word web to write song lyrics about your topic. Song lyrics are basically poems set to music. Your lyrics can rhyme or not, but should describe and express a point of view, make sense, and be of high interest to a listener. Write your draft in the space below. Then write a neat, final copy in ink *on a separate sheet of paper.*

Use this rubric to evaluate your song lyrics. Make changes to your lyrics if you need to.

Score	Description
3	The song lyrics are clearly relevant to the topic. They include supporting details and descriptive terms from the word web and express a point of view or lesson. There are no spelling or grammar errors.
2	The song lyrics are somewhat relevant to the topic. They include some supporting details from the word web and express a vague point of view or lesson. There are some spelling or grammar errors.
1	The song lyrics are not relevant to the topic. They include few supporting details from the word web and lack a strong point of view or lesson. There are many spelling or grammar errors.

Timeline Skills

Analyze the Unit 3 timeline in your book. Also think about what you have learned in this unit. Then answer the following questions.

1. What kinds of settlements were first established in West Africa?

2. Trans-Saharan trade began with transporting what item across the desert?

3. For about how many years did the Nok thrive in West Africa?

4. How many years after North Africans began trans-Saharan trade were camels introduced to the region?

5. What were three primary occupations of Jenne-Jeno's 20,000 residents?

6. On what was the kingdom of Ghana's economy based?

7. What led to the decline of Ghana?

8. Which ruler of Mali was the first to become a devout Muslim?

9. What West African empire rose to power after Mali?

10. Where was the University of Sankore?

Critical Thinking

Use the timeline and the chapters in the unit to answer the following questions.

11. Explain how the Nok's ability to make tools out of iron ultimately contributed to the growth of settlements in West Africa.

12. Identify and then discuss two factors that led to the development of trans-Saharan trade.

13. Discuss three ways that Islam had an impact on West Africa.

14. If you could add three more events to this timeline, which would they be? List each event, and explain why you think it is important enough to add to the timeline.

    a.

    b.

    c.

UNIT

Imperial China

Geography Challenge

Chapter 15: The Political Development of Imperial China

Which method of selecting officials led to the best leaders for China?

Chapter 16: China Develops a New Economy

How did the Chinese improve their economy during the Tang and Song dynasties?

Chapter 17: Chinese Discoveries and Inventions

How have medieval Chinese discoveries and inventions influenced the modern world?

Chapter 18: China's Contacts with the Outside World

How did the foreign-contact policies of three medieval Chinese dynasties affect China?

Timeline Challenge

Asia

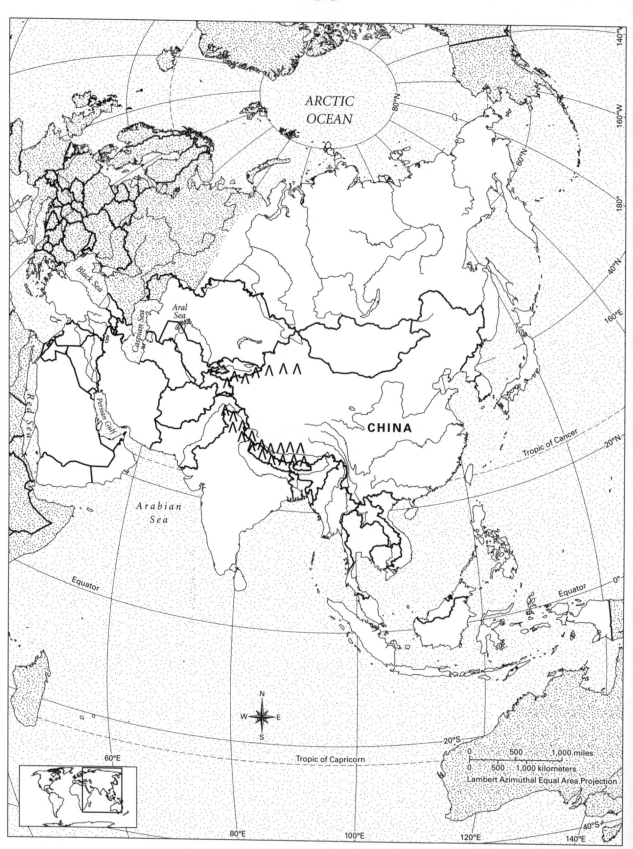

ARCTIC OCEAN

Black Sea

Aral Sea

Caspian Sea

Red Sea

Persian Gulf

CHINA

Tropic of Cancer

Arabian Sea

Equator

Equator

Tropic of Capricorn

0   500   1,000 miles
0   500   1,000 kilometers
Lambert Azimuthal Equal Area Projection

80°E   100°E   120°E   140°E

60°E

Geography Skills

Analyze the maps in "Setting the Stage" for Unit 4 in your book. Then answer the following questions and fill out the map as directed.

1. Label the Sea of Japan (East Sea), the Yellow Sea, the East China Sea, the South China Sea, the Indian Ocean, and the Bay of Bengal. Which of these bodies of water lies farthest north?

2. Locate the deserts that lie in and near imperial China. Label them on your map.

3. Suppose traders were traveling from China to the Mediterranean region. What physical features in China would they have had to cross?

4. Draw a line showing the shortest sea route from China to the eastern coast of India. Begin at the mouth of the Chang Jiang (Yangtze River). Why might knowledge of the compass have allowed the Chinese to have been, at one time, a major sea power?

5. During the 200s B.C.E., a Chinese emperor ordered his people to connect walls built by earlier rulers. The completed project, the Great Wall of China, extended along the northern border of China. It was meant to protect the Chinese from invasions that came from the north. Why do you think the emperor was more concerned about attacks from this direction than any other?

6. Label the Huang He (Yellow River), the Chang Jiang (Yangtze River), the North China Plain, and the Chang Jiang Basins. Land near these rivers was heavily populated. Why might this be so?

7. Label the Plateau of Tibet, the Tian Shan, and the Himalayas. In what part of China are they located? Why would these features have made sea trade more popular than overland trade?

Critical Thinking

Answer the following questions in complete sentences.

8. While it took around five hundred years for the Buddhist religion to reach China from India, it took more than twice that long for Christianity to reach China from Europe. What geographical factors might explain this difference?

9. Look at the land to the north of the North China Plain. Why might the people living in this area have attacked those living around the Huang He (Yellow River)?

10. How did China's geography influence the directions in which rulers chose to expand their empires?

11. What geographical features of China led to the growth of cities? Explain your answer.

The Political Development of Imperial China

Which method of selecting officials led to the best leaders for China?

PREVIEW

Suppose that you had to choose someone, like a friend or relative, to make decisions for you. This person might need to make decisions about important issues, such as your finances or your future. Which of these people would you trust most to make decisions for you?

- someone who is from another country
- someone who is rich
- someone who is considered an excellent student

Explain the reasons for your choice in the space below.

READING NOTES

Key Content Terms

As you complete the Reading Notes, use these terms in your answers.

emperor	warlord
imperial	aristocracy
dynasty	civil service examination
bureaucracy	meritocracy

Section 15.2

1. According to the Mandate of Heaven, when can people overthrow the emperor?

2. What is a *bureaucracy?* What happened when the bureaucracy in China became corrupt?

3. What happened to China when the Han dynasty lost the Mandate of Heaven? Who reunited China?

4. Draw a simple symbol for the term or concept you believe is the most important from this section. Include a label for your symbol.

Section 15.3

1. Who were scholar-officials?

2. The examination for scholar-officials was mainly based on what body of knowledge?

3. During the Tang dynasty, why did aristocrats continue to hold most government offices?

4. Draw a simple symbol for the term or concept you believe is the most important from this section. Include a label for your symbol.

Section 15.4

1. According to emperors and scholars, knowledge of the ideas of Confucius would produce what type of government official?

2. How did the process of becoming a government official change during the Song period?

3. Why did people in medieval China want government jobs?

4. Draw a simple symbol for the term or concept you believe is the most important from this section. Include a label for your symbol.

Section 15.5

1. Why did Kublai Khan end the system of civil service exams?

2. Whom did Kublai Khan choose to fill important government positions?

3. What happened to Chinese scholars under Mongol rule?

4. Draw a simple symbol for the term or concept you believe is the most important from this section. Include a label for your symbol.

After reading this section, complete the T-chart below by adding at least three details that support the statements in each column.

Hiring Scholar-Officials Helped China	Hiring Scholar-Officials Hurt China

PROCESSING

Based on the activity and reading, determine which method of selecting Chinese officials you think led to the best leaders. *On a separate sheet of paper,* create a sensory figure for that type of official (Aristocrat, Foreigner, or Scholar) that shows what makes them good leaders.

A sensory figure is a simple drawing of a figure with labels giving *at least four* statements of what that person might be seeing, hearing, saying, feeling, or doing. For example, if you choose Foreigners, you might draw a heart on the person's chest. Then you might write, "I feel loyalty to my emperor Kublai Khan, not to the Chinese people."

China Develops a New Economy

16

How did the Chinese improve their economy during the Tang and Song dynasties?

Look around your classroom. What characteristics—things that make a classroom different from other types of rooms, such as a bedroom, kitchen, or gym—do you see? Identify four characteristics unique to a classroom. Then, in each square below, create a simple sketch to illustrate each characteristic.

Four Characteristics of a Classroom

READING NOTES

Key Content Terms

As you complete the Reading Notes, use these terms in your answers.

economy   currency

commerce   urbanization

Section 16.2

Fill in the graphic organizer below by doing the following:

- List one reason for agricultural change in each box at the top.
- List at least five characteristics of the new agriculture in the center box.
- List at least three results of these changes in the bottom box.

Reasons for Agricultural Changes

Characteristics of the New Agriculture

Results of Agricultural Changes

Section 16.3

Fill in the graphic organizer below by doing the following:

- List one reason for the growth in China's trade and commerce in each box at the top.
- List at least five characteristics of China's commercial growth in the center box.
- List at least two results of these changes in the bottom box.

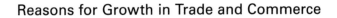

Reasons for Growth in Trade and Commerce

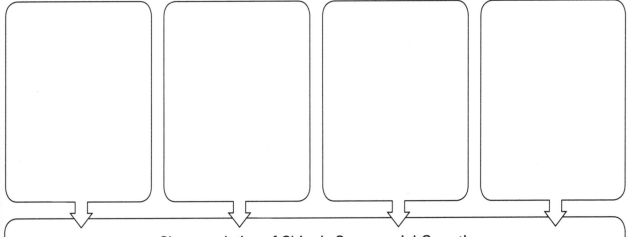

Characteristics of China's Commercial Growth

Results of Growth in Trade and Commerce

Fill in the graphic organizer below by doing the following:

- List one reason for urbanization in China in each box at the top.
- List at least five characteristics of China's cities in the center box.
- List at least two results of urbanization in the bottom box.

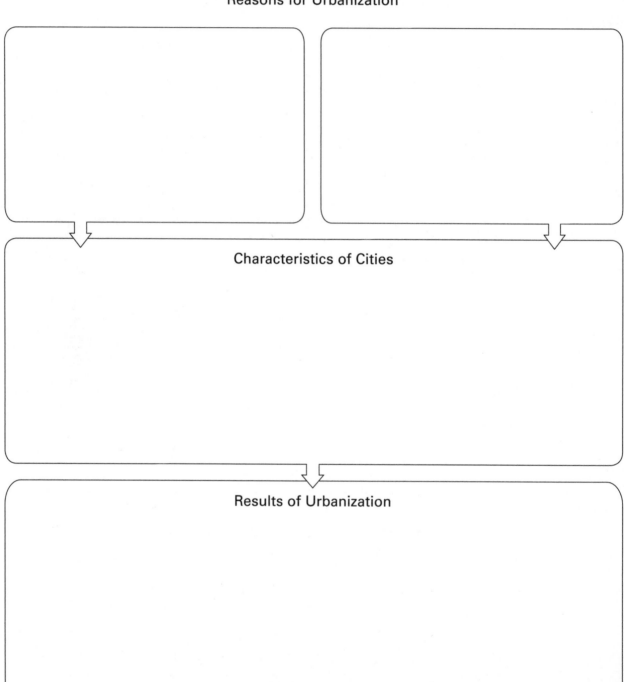

Reasons for Urbanization

Characteristics of Cities

Results of Urbanization

PROCESSING

On another sheet of paper, create an advertisement promoting the aspect of society (agriculture, commerce, or urbanization) you believe most improved the medieval Chinese economy. Your advertisement can be a poster, billboard, flyer, commercial, or any other medium used for advertising. It should meet the following requirements:

- It should clearly state what aspect of society you believe most improved the Chinese economy.

- It should contain a slogan and three ways in which that aspect of society improved the economy.

- It should include an image or decorative art illustrating that aspect of medieval China.

You may use the space below to create a planning sketch for your advertisement.

Chinese Discoveries and Inventions

How have medieval Chinese discoveries and inventions influenced the modern world?

PREVIEW

In this activity, you will learn how to draw Chinese characters.

Drawing the Strokes of a Chinese Character

Strokes are drawn from top to bottom and left to right. Strokes are also drawn in one continuous motion. Do not lift your pen until you have completed an entire stroke. Follow your teacher's directions and the numbers in the diagram for each character below to reproduce each stroke. Then practice writing each character.

Character	Meaning	Practice Writing Your Character Here
日	Day	
木	Wood	
山	Mountain	

READING NOTES

Key Content Terms

As you complete the Reading Notes, use these terms in your answers.

movable type   mass-produce   gunpowder   inoculate

Sections 17.2 to 17.6

Part One

If your class is doing the activity for this chapter, complete all steps in Part One.
(Note: If your class is not doing the activity, skip Part One.)

As you analyze each placard in the activity, do the following:

1. Look at the title of the placard, then skim through Sections 17.2 to 17.6 to find the section or subsection that discusses the placard.

2. Next to the placard letter in each box below, record the name of the discovery or invention.

3. Record the related section number and title.

4. Write a one-sentence summary of the discovery or invention.

5. Write a one-sentence summary of its influence on the modern world.

6. Draw the Chinese character(s) using the method you practiced in the Preview activity.

A:

Section 17.___:

Summary of invention:

Summary of influence:

Character:

B:

Section 17.___:

Summary of invention:

Summary of influence:

Character:

C:

Section 17.___:

Summary of invention:

Summary of influence:

Character:

D:

Section 17.___:

Summary of invention:

Summary of influence:

Character:

E:

Section 17.___:

Summary of invention:

Summary of influence:

Character:

F:

Section 17.___:

Summary of invention:

Summary of influence:

Character:

G:

Section 17.___:

Summary of invention:

Summary of influence:

Character:

H:

Section 17.___:

Summary of invention:

Summary of influence:

Character:

I:

Section 17.___:

Summary of invention:

Summary of influence:

Character:

J:

Section 17.___:

Summary of invention:

Summary of influence:

Character:

After completing the Reading Notes for all placards, place each placard letter in the appropriate place on the spectrum below, based on what you think its influence is on the modern world.

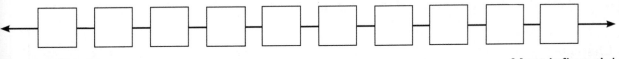

Least Influential
to the Modern World

Most Influential
to the Modern World

Part 2

Skim Sections 17.2 through 17.6. Then, find 11 Chinese discoveries and inventions that match the descriptions below. Draw a symbol to represent the invention, and write the name of the invention on the blank line, as shown in the example.

Section 17.2

Speeded up travel on rivers and lakes. *paddlewheel boat*

Improved boat construction. _____

Made bridges flatter and stronger. _____

Section 17.3

Made from bark; became an important industry.

_____

Led to the printing of modern style books. _____

Stronger and lighter than iron. _____

Section 17.4

Made from gunpowder mixed with oil. _____

Caused a loud sound when exploded. _____

A slingshot-like war machine to shoot arrows.

_____

Small bomb thrown by hand. _____

Section 17.5

Made from woodblock printing on thick paper.

_____

Section 17.6

Poisonous smoke used to kill germs. _____

PROCESSING

Create a scroll that celebrates Chinese discoveries and inventions.

1. Review your Reading Notes to determine the four Chinese discoveries or inventions that you believe have had the greatest influence on the world.

2. *On a separate sheet of paper,* write a short paragraph that gives at least two reasons why you selected each discovery or invention.

3. Create a scroll from a piece of drawing paper and partially curl the ends of the paper to look like a scroll.

4. Write the Chinese character and the English word for each discovery or invention. Also create a colorful illustration or symbol for it. Draw a decorative border around each discovery or invention.

Your scroll should look something like this:

羅針盤

Compass

China's Contacts with the Outside World

How did the foreign-contact policies of three medieval Chinese dynasties affect China?

PREVIEW

Read the situation below.

The Johnsons have just moved to a new neighborhood. They are debating whether to have an open- or closed-door policy toward their neighbors. If they have an open-door policy, they will invite the neighbors to parties, ask for and perform favors for them, and borrow from and lend things to them. If they have a closed-door policy, they will keep to themselves and not interact with their neighbors at all.

In the T-chart below, write two arguments in favor of the Johnsons following an open-door policy and two arguments in favor of a closed-door policy. One example is done for each.

Arguments for an Open-Door Policy	 **Arguments for a Closed-Door Policy**
An open-door policy is a good idea because if the Johnsons are friendly with their neighbors, their neighbors will share information about local services.	A closed-door policy is good because if the Johnsons are not friendly with the neighbors, the neighbors won't ask to borrow their things.

READING NOTES

Key Content Terms

As you complete the Reading Notes, use these terms in your answers.

Mongols   Ming

maritime   tributary

If you are doing the activity for this chapter, complete all steps in the Reading Notes for each section. *(Note: If you are not doing the activity, skip Step 1 for each section.)*

Section 18.2

Step 1: Read along with the first dialogue on Student Handout 18.

Step 2: Answer the following questions about Section 18.2.

1. In the space below, list at least six countries with whom China had contact during the Tang dynasty (through traders, merchants, missionaries, or visitors).

2. Describe how attitudes and policies changed toward the end of the Tang dynasty in regard to each of the following:

    *   Foreigners:

    *   Buddhists:

    *   Trade routes:

Step 3: Answer the following question, using supporting details from your Reading Notes: To what degree did emperors of the Tang dynasty pursue a closed- or an open-door policy? Then, place an X at the appropriate place on the spectrum to indicate your answer.

Closed-Door
Policy

Open-Door
Policy

Section 18.3

Step 1: Read along with the second dialogue on Student Handout 18.

Step 2: Answer the following questions about Section 18.3.

1. List four ways in which China was affected by thriving trade during the Yuan dynasty.

2. Describe the role of foreigners in China during the Yuan dynasty. Then, explain how the Chinese felt about this.

Step 3: Answer the following question, using supporting details from your Reading Notes: To what degree did emperors of the Yuan dynasty pursue a closed- or an open-door policy? Then, place an X at the appropriate place on the spectrum to indicate your answer.

Closed-Door
Policy

Open-Door
Policy

Step 1: Read along with the third dialogue on Student Handout 18.

Step 2: Answer the following questions about Section 18.4.

1. What belief led China to acquire tributaries during the Ming dynasty?

2. Explain the purpose and result of Zheng He's expeditions.

3. Describe what happened as the Ming dynasty turned inward in the mid-1400s.

Step 3: Answer the following question, using supporting details from your Reading Notes: To what degree did emperors of the Ming dynasty pursue a closed- or an open-door policy? Then, place and X at the appropriate place on the spectrum to indicate your answer.

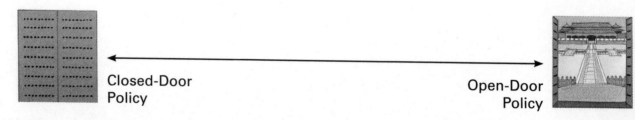

Closed-Door
Policy

Open-Door
Policy

PROCESSING

You are a Ming emperor. You must decide whether China should have an open-door policy or a closed-door policy toward foreigners. In the space below, write your decision in the form of a royal proclamation. Then give five reasons that support your decision. Illustrate each of your reasons. For example, you might write, "Contact with foreigners benefits China because foreign merchants bring us luxuries, such as pearls." You might illustrate this sentence with a pearl.

Preparing to Write: Story Mapping a Narrative

The story, or narrative, of Zheng He's life is one of the great sea adventures. Is there an event in your life that was fun or exciting, such as a theme-park visit, favorite vacation, or a special celebration? Choose an event in your life that you would like to write about. Then complete the story map below to plan your own, or autobiographical, narrative.

Topic/Title	
Setting	
Character(s)	
Beginning Actions or Events	
Middle Actions or Events	
Conclusion	

Writing an Autobiographical Narrative

On a separate sheet of paper, use your story map to write your autobiographical narrative. Your narrative should be written in the first person, meaning from your point of view. It should also include a beginning, a middle, and an ending and be from 500 to 700 words long.

Use this rubric to evaluate your autobiographical narrative. Make changes to your narrative if you need to.

Score	Description
3	The narrative is written in the first person, includes a clear beginning, middle, and ending and is from 500 to 700 words long. There are no spelling or grammatical errors
2	The narrative is written in the first person, includes a beginning, middle, and ending and is at least 500 words long. There are some spelling or grammatical errors.
1	The narrative is written in the first person, includes a vague beginning, middle, and ending or is missing main plot points, and is fewer than 500 words long. There are many spelling or grammatical errors.

Timeline Skills

Analyze the Unit 4 timeline in your book. Also think about what you have learned in this unit. Then answer the following questions.

1. For how many years did the Han dynasty rule China?

2. What religion spread to China under the Tang dynasty, and where did it come from?

3. During which dynasty were officials chosen by merit-based exams?

4. What was the result of increased food production during the Song dynasty?

5. What invention made written materials more widely available?

6. About what year was the art of papermaking developed in China? Why was this an important invention?

7. How many years passed between the fall of the Tang dynasty and the rise of the Song dynasty?

8. Which foreign group ruled China during the Yuan dynasty?

9. During which dynasty did Marco Polo travel through China?

10. During which dynasty did Zheng He make his voyages?

Critical Thinking

Use the timeline and the chapters in the unit to answer the following questions.

11. Which do you think most contributed to a high quality of life in China during the Song dynasty: agricultural changes or trade? Explain your answer.

12. The Chinese made many discoveries and inventions between about 200 C.E. and 1400 C.E. What two inventions do you believe have most affected life today, and why?

13. Compare the process of appointing government officials under the Song and Yuan dynasties.

14. If you could add three more events to this timeline, which would they be? List each event, and explain why you think it is important enough to add to the timeline.

    a.

    b.

    c.

Japan During Medieval Times

Japan

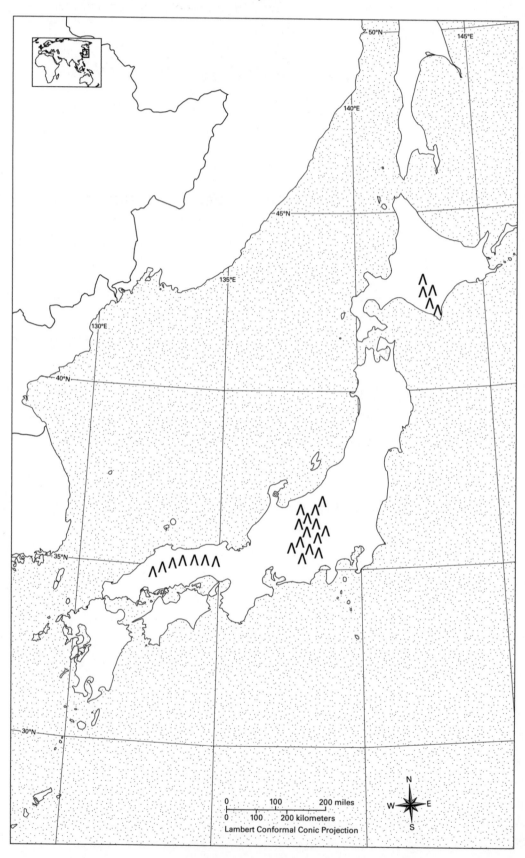

Geography Skills

Analyze the maps in "Setting the Stage" for Unit 5 in your book. Then answer the following questions and fill out the map as directed.

1. Locate the Japanese islands of Honshu, Kyushu, Hokkaido, and Shikoku. Label them. About how far does Japan extend from north to south? About how many miles wide is Japan at its widest point?

2. Label the countries that are closest to Japan. At what point is the distance between Japan and the Asian continent the shortest? Is the distance from Japan to the Asian continent shortest between Japan and Korea, or is it shortest between Japan and China?

3. Locate the Kanto Plain. Label it. On which Japanese island is it located?

4. Locate and label the ancient cities of Nara and Kyoto.

5. Which percent—90 percent, 60 percent, or 15 percent—do you think best expresses the amount of land Japan can use for agriculture?

6. Label the Sea of Japan (East Sea), the East China Sea, and the Pacific Ocean. In what ways did these bodies of water influence Japan's history?

7. Locate the Chugoku Range, the Japanese Alps, and the Hidaka Range. Label them.

8. Use the "Political Features of the World" map in the back of your book to answer the following question: What present-day country lies to the east of Japan, across the Pacific Ocean?

Critical Thinking

Answer the following questions in complete sentences.

9. Which of the Japanese islands do you think became the center of power in Japan? Explain your answer.

10. Describe one advantage and one disadvantage of Japan's geography.

11. The Kanto Plain is the most populated area in Japan. Why do you think this is so?

12. As you have learned, Japan first developed in isolation because it is surrounded by water. Do you think oceans and seas are significant barriers to the movement of people, goods, and ideas today? Explain your answer.

The Influence of Neighboring Cultures on Japan

In what ways did neighboring cultures influence Japan?

The items listed below can all be found in the United States. In the chart, list the aspect of American culture each item represents. For example, an item might represent art, literature, religion, government, clothing, music, or food. Then state whether you think the item was first developed in the United States or was borrowed from another country.

Item	Aspect of Culture Represented	From the U.S. or Borrowed from Another Country?
piano		
fire engine		
blue jeans		
ice cream		
television		

READING NOTES

Key Content Terms

As you complete the Reading Notes, use these terms in your answers.

Prince Shotoku   meditation

Shinto   pagoda

Section 19.2

1. Label the following four countries on the map below: Japan, India, China, and Korea. Then color each in a different color.

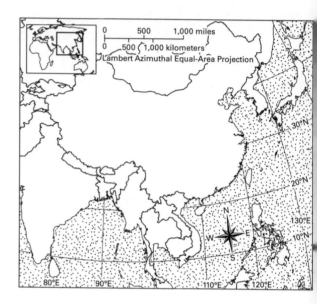

2. How did Empress Suiko and Prince Shotoku come to power?

3. For each category below, circle the word or phrase that best describes Japanese society and family life when Empress Suiko and Prince Shotoku began their rule.

Type of Society	industrial society	agricultural society
Main Crop	rice	wheat
Family Life	centered around the mother	dominated by the father
Government	one all-powerful emperor	power divided among uji

4. List three ways by which knowledge of mainland culture came to Japan.

   •

   •

   •

If you are doing the activity, complete all questions in the following sections of Reading Notes. *(Note: If you are not doing the activity, skip Question 1 in each section.)*

Follow these steps to complete the Reading Notes for Sections 19.3 to 19.10.

1. Complete each chart.
2. Color the country where the cultural idea developed. Use the same color that you used to color your map in Section 19.2 of the Reading Notes.
3. Use arrows to show the path by which the idea reached Japan. It may have come directly to Japan or traveled through other countries to get there.
4. Respond to the statement(s) below the chart.

Section 19.3

1.

Letters of the Matching Cards		
Country the Card Represents		

2. Describe Japan's government before it was influenced by countries on the Asian mainland.

3. Describe the new ideas about government that Japan adopted and any changes the Japanese made to these ideas.

Section 19.4

1.

Letters of the Matching Cards		
Country the Card Represents		

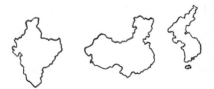

2. Describe the ideas that Japan adopted for its new capital city.

3. What were the main differences between the capital cities of Japan and China?

Section 19.5

1.

Letters of the Matching Cards		
Country the Card Represents		

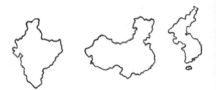

2. Describe Japan's religion before it was influenced by countries on the mainland.

3. Describe the new religion that Japan adopted and any changes the Japanese made to this religion.

Section 19.6

1.

Letters of the Matching Cards		
Country the Card Represents		

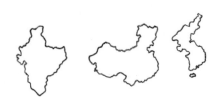

2. Describe Japan's language before it was influenced by countries on the mainland.

3. Describe the new writing that Japan adopted and any changes the Japanese made to this style of writing.

Section 19.7

1.

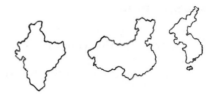

Letters of the Matching Cards		
Country the Card Represents		

2. Describe the new form of poetry that the Japanese developed.

Section 19.8

1.

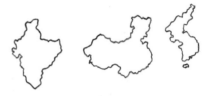

Letters of the Matching Cards		
Country the Card Represents		

2. Describe Japanese sculpture before it was influenced by countries on the mainland.

3. Explain how Japanese sculptures of Buddha are similar to those from China and Korea. How are they different?

Section 19.9

1.

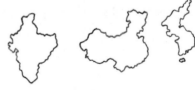

Letters of the Matching Cards		
Country the Card Represents		

2. Describe the new style of architecture that Japan adopted.

Section 19.10

1.

Letters of the Matching Cards		
Country the Card Represents		

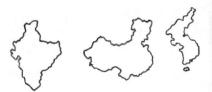

2. Describe Japan's music before it was influenced by countries on the Asian mainland.

3. Describe the new musical instrument that the Japanese adopted.

PROCESSING

Suppose that you are a visitor from mainland Asia to Japan in the 9th century. *On a separate sheet of paper,* write a letter to a friend back home describing Japanese society and culture. Your letter must include the following:

- a greeting to your friend and the name of the country he or she lives in
- descriptions of at least two elements of Japanese society or culture that are the *same or similar* to your own culture
- descriptions of at least two elements of Japanese society or culture that are *different* from your own culture
- a proper closing and a signature

Heian-kyo: The Heart of Japan's Golden Age

What was life like for aristocrats during the Heian period?

Examine the image your teacher is projecting. Suppose that you are one of the people in this image. You are being shown into this house for the first time.

1. What are some things you might expect to see?

2. Notice the man standing in the middle of the small group in the lower right-hand corner of the painting. He seems to be pointing at the home. What do you imagine he is saying to the group of men?

READING NOTES

Key Content Terms

As you complete the Reading Notes, use these terms in your answers.

Heian period   courtier

golden age   *Tale of Genji*

Section 20.2

1. Why did the emperor move the Japanese capital from Nara to Heian-kyo?

2. Complete the statement being made by the Heian lady below using the following words: *gardens, stone wall, screens.*

My life in Heian-kyo is filled with beauty and elegance. For instance, the mansion I live in has . . .

If you are doing the activity, complete all questions in the following sections of the Reading Notes. *(Note: If you are not doing the activity, skip Question 1 in each section.)*

Section 20.3

1. Station A: How did you behave toward Fujiwara Michinaga? Why?

2. List two ways the Fujiwara family was able to exercise power despite their not being the formal rulers of Japan.

3. Sketch and label a drawing to illustrate an important idea about the Fujiwara family.

Section 20.4

1. Station B: What did you do with the fan? Why?

2. What determined the rank a person held during the Heian period?

3. Quickly sketch and label a diagram to illustrate the different ranks in the Heian court hierarchy. For example, you might draw a ladder with nine rungs, each representing one rank.

Section 20.5

1. Station C: What tips did you give a Heian woman about how to apply cosmetics?

2. How was a person judged during the Heian period?

3. Quickly sketch and label a drawing to illustrate an important idea about Heian beauty, fashion, and manners. For example, you might draw and color the face of a woman who would have been considered beautiful.

Section 20.6

1. Station G: Write the number of times you were able to kick the ball to each other without it touching the ground and the number of stones you were able to balance on your finger.

    Ball _____   Stones _____

2. Match each of the following forms of Japanese recreation or entertainment with the correct description.

    _____ Festival of the Snake   a. large men try to throw each other out of a ring
    _____ bugaku   b. young women try balance stones on one finger
    _____ sumo wrestling   c. cups are floated in a stream
    _____ rango   d. courtiers kick a leather ball back and forth
    _____ kemari   e. dancers wear masks and act out simple stories

3. Quickly sketch and label a drawing to illustrate an important idea about entertainment or recreation during the Heian period.

Section 20.7

1. Station D: Which work of art did you praise, Painting 1 or Painting 2? Why?

2. How did the process of carving statues change during this period?

3. How did painting change during this period?

Section 20.8

1. Station E: Which book did you borrow from the nobleman? Why?

2. Explain how poetry was part of daily life in Heian-kyo.

3. Identify three reasons why the *Tale of Genji* is significant even today.

Section 20.9

1. Station F: What should be your attitude toward the poor if you want the aristocrats to accept you?

2. List three reasons why the Heian period came to an end.

3. Quickly sketch and label a drawing to illustrate an important idea about the end of the Heian period.

Section 20.10

Complete the spoke diagram by describing ways
in which the Heian period influences present-day
Japan for each of the three categories.

Literature

**Influences of the
Heian Period on
Modern Japan**

Poetry

Music

PROCESSING

On a separate sheet of paper, write a paragraph answering the Essential Question:

What was life like for aristocrats during the Heian period?

The Rise of the Warrior Class in Japan

What was the role of the samurai in the military society of medieval Japan?

PREVIEW

Use the list below to check off the skills, knowledge, and values that you believe should be taught to American soldiers. You can check as many as you think are important.

_____ 1. Swimming

_____ 2. The use of a rifle

_____ 3. Driving a motor vehicle

_____ 4. Acceptance of hardships without complaint

_____ 5. The use of a knife

_____ 6. Dancing

_____ 7. The use of a computer

_____ 8. Basic religious beliefs

_____ 9. Language of the enemy

_____ 10. World history

_____ 11. Geneva Convention (the rules of war)

_____ 12. Literature appreciation

_____ 13. Dinner manners

_____ 14. The operation of a two-way radio

_____ 15. Code of Military Conduct (outlines how soldiers should behave during battle or when captured)

_____ 16. Art appreciation

_____ 17. Unquestioning obedience to orders

_____ 18. The operation of a grenade launcher

READING NOTES

Key Content Terms

As you complete the Reading Notes, use these terms in your answers.

shogun   Amida Buddhism

samurai   Zen Buddhism

daimyo   Bushido

martial arts   restoration

Section 21.2

1. Look at the illustrations at right. Explain how these three figures are related. Tell what each one promises the other two.

Shogun   **Daimyo**   **Samurai**

2. How did the government of Japan change in 1603?

Section 21.3

1. On the drawing at right, label three important parts of the samurai's armor.

2. Label the samurai's weapon and explain the purposes of the long sword he carried.

3. Add one additional weapon to the drawing. Label it.

Section 21.4

1. Write one interesting detail about a samurai's training in archery.

2. Tell what a samurai might do if he lost or broke his sword.

3. In the speech bubble, write what a samurai might say before a battle.

Section 21.5

1. In the thought bubble, write what a samurai should think about every day to overcome his fear of death.

2. Give an example of how samurai were trained to endure pain and suffering.

3. Explain why samurai were trained to always be alert, and list one way that samurai were trained to be prepared.

Section 21.6

1. In the speech bubble, explain what calligraphy is and why a samurai was expected to practice it.

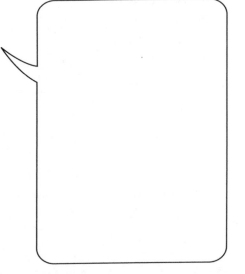

2. What is *haiku?*

Section 21.7

Around the samurai, draw and label three objects a samurai would see when he or she attended a tea ceremony.

Section 21.8

1. Explain how a samurai would prove his or her devotion to Amida Buddha.

2. Explain how one can achieve enlightenment according to Zen Buddhism.

3. In the thought bubble, write a classic koan that samurai would meditate on.

Section 21.9

1. Explain what Bushido was and how it governed a samurai's life.

2. In the thought bubble, write how the samurai believed he should act toward his lord.

Section 21.10

1. Draw a 12th-century samurai woman next to the male samurai. The size of the woman should show her status in the 12th century as compared to a samurai man at this time.

2. How did the position of samurai women change from the 12th to the 17th century?

Section 21.11

Compare and contrast medieval European feudal society with the samurai society of Japan by completing the Venn diagram below. Consider these questions:

- Who were the military leaders in Europe and Japan during these periods? How were they alike? How were they different?

- Who were large landowners in Europe and Japan during these periods? How were they alike? How were they different?

- Who were the warriors in Europe and Japan during these periods? How were they alike? How were they different?

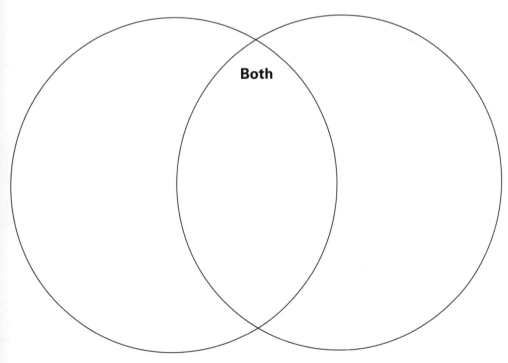

Both

Samurai Society of Japan

Western Europe in the Middle Ages

1. Describe one way that the Japanese military followed the samurai code during World War II.

2. List three ways that modern Japan still feels the influence of the era of the samurai.

PROCESSING

Suppose you that have been asked to create a class schedule for a young person who is new to samurai training. *On a separate sheet of a paper,* copy and complete the training schedule below by doing the following:

- In the first column, choose four different areas of training that were necessary for samurai. List each one as a separate class.
- In the second column, describe what samurai students will learn in this course.
- In the third column, explain what the purpose of the training is or why this training is important.

An example has been done for you.

Training Schedule	Description of Course	Purpose of Training
Class Period 1: Military Training	Students will learn how to shoot with a bow and arrow accurately while riding on the back of a galloping horse. They will also learn fencing and martial arts.	Samurai must be able to fight ably and courageously in battle. They must learn how to master both physical and mental techniques that will make them good warriors.
Class Period 2:		
Class Period 3:		
Class Period 4:		
Class Period 5:		

Preparing to Write: Comparing and Contrasting

Read the passage about the Japanese woman warrior Hangaku Gozen. Then, use what you have read about Tomoe Gozen and Hangaku Gozen to complete the Venn diagram below.

Hangaku Gozen, . . . became famous after the Genpei War. She belonged to the Taira clan, the Minamoto clan's enemies. In 1201, she led an army of 3,000 soldiers against more than 10,000 enemy warriors. She was wounded and taken prisoner. There are many explanations as to what happened to her after she was taken prisoner. She appears in the Mirror of the East, *or* Azuma Kagami, *an epic story about the years 1180–1266. It was later written down in many versions. Historians think that she was probably a real person that grew into a legend.*

—From "Women Warriors of Japan," by Ellis Amdur, 1996

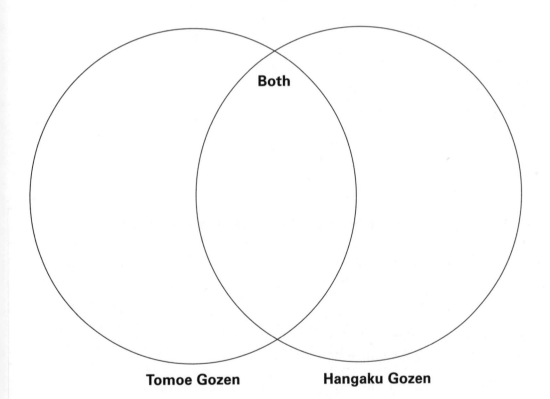

Both

Tomoe Gozen   Hangaku Gozen

Writing a Summary

Use your Venn diagram and what you have read to write a summary that compares and contrasts Tomoe Gozen and Hangaku Gozen. Your summary should include a topic sentence, at least two paragraphs, and a conclusion.

Use this rubric to evaluate your summary. Make changes to your summary if you need to.

Score	Description
3	The summary clearly compares and contrasts the two figures. Each is well constructed with a topic sentence, many supporting details, and a conclusion. There are no spelling or grammar errors.
2	The summary compares and contrasts the two figures. Each has a topic sentence, supporting details, and a conclusion. There are some spelling or grammar errors.
1	The summary only vaguely compares and contrasts the two figures. It lacks a topic sentence, supporting details, or a conclusion. There are many spelling or grammar errors.

Timeline Skills

Analyze the Unit 5 timeline in your book. Also think about what you have learned in this unit. Then answer the following questions.

1. From what country did Buddhism come to Japan?

2. How did Prince Shotoku influence Japanese culture?

3. After what country's capital was the new Japanese capital modeled?

4. List three events that occurred during the Heian Period.

5. What was unusual about Fujiwara Michinaga's rule?

6. What is the significance of the *Tale of Genji?*

7. For how many years did civil war persist in Japan before Minamoto Yoritomo seized control and set up a military government?

8. For about how many centuries did Japan have a feudal system of lords, vassals, and samurai?

Critical Thinking

Use the timeline and the chapters in the unit to answer the following questions.

9. For each society listed below, identify and explain two ways that society's culture influenced Japanese culture.

    a. Korea:

    b. China:

10. Identify one example of literature and one style of art created in Japan during the Heian period.

11. Explain three different aspects of samurai training.

12. If you could add three more events to this timeline, which would they be? List each event, and explain why you think it is important enough to add to the timeline.

    a.

    b.

    c.

Civilizations of the Americas

Mexico, Central America, and South America

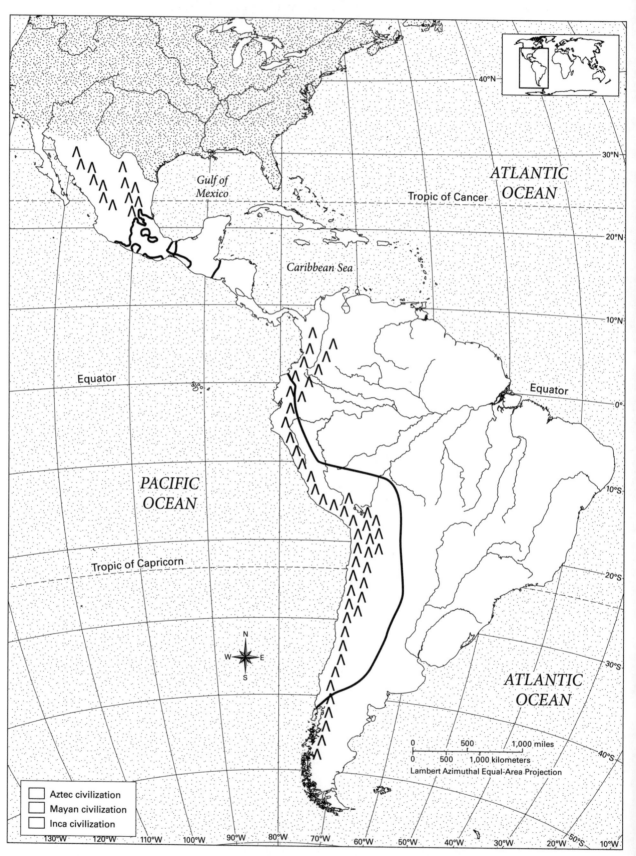

Gulf of
Mexico

Tropic of Cancer

*ATLANTIC
OCEAN*

40°N

30°N

20°N

Caribbean Sea

10°N

Equator

Equator

0°

*PACIFIC
OCEAN*

10°S

Tropic of Capricorn

20°S

N
W — E
S

30°S

*ATLANTIC
OCEAN*

| 0 | 500 | 1,000 miles |

| 0 | 500 | 1,000 kilometers |
Lambert Azimuthal Equal-Area Projection

40°S

☐ Aztec civilization
☐ Mayan civilization
☐ Inca civilization

50°S

130°W 120°W 110°W 100°W 90°W 80°W 70°W 60°W 50°W 40°W 30°W 20°W 10°W

Geography Skills

Analyze the maps in "Setting the Stage" for Unit 6 in your book. Then answer the following questions and fill out the map as directed.

1. Locate the area of the Mayan civilization. Shade it on your map and in the key.

2. Locate the area of the Aztec civilization. Shade it on your map and in the key.

3. Locate the area of the Incan civilization. Shade it on your map and in the key.

4. Locate the Sierra Madre Occidental, the Sierra Madre Oriental, the Andes Mountains, the Mexico Plateau, the Yucatán Peninsula, and the Amazon River. Label them on your map.

5. According the map in your book, what is the elevation and principal climate zone of the land in central Mexico?

6. How would you predict that elevation and climate might affect the way the Aztecs lived?

7. About how high is the land in the northern Yucatán Peninsula? In the southern Yucatán Peninsula?

8. Which climate zone is in the northern Yucatán Peninsula? Which climate zone is southern Yucatán Peninsula?

9. What challenges do you think climate and elevation might have posed for the Mayas?

10. What is the elevation and climate of the land in western South America?

11. What impact do you think elevation and climate might have had on Incan life?

Critical Thinking

Answer the following questions in complete sentences.

12. Based on physical features and climate, which civilization would you predict had the largest city? Why?

13. In which civilization do you think it would have been easiest for people to have an economy based on agriculture? Why? Where do you think agriculture would have been most challenging? Why?

14. What do people need in order to trade? Which civilization do you predict had an extensive system of trade? Why?

15. Look at the geographic features of all three civilizations. What did they have in common that enabled them to thrive?

The Mayas

What led to the rise, flourishing, and fall of the Mayan civilization?

PREVIEW

Follow your teacher's directions to create a Mayan social pyramid. After working with your class to create a pyramid, answer the following questions about your experience:

• What do you think this pyramid represents?

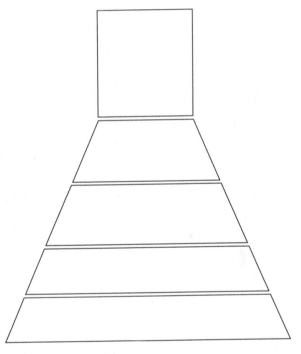

• Record one or two clues from the Preview activity that tell you what types of people might be at each level on the pyramid.

• How do you think the class structure of the Mayas affected people's lives?

READING NOTES

Key Content Terms

As you complete the Reading Notes, use these terms in your answers.

Mayas	ceremonial center	social pyramid	sacrifice
Mesoamerica	hieroglyphic	ritual	slash-and-burn agriculture

Section 22.2

1. On the map below, do the following:

   - Draw in the boundary of the Mayan civilization. Then color in the appropriate box on the key to match the boundary color.

   - Use different colors to shade the northern lowlands, southern lowlands, and highlands. Then shade the appropriate boxes in the key.

   - Label the Yucatán Peninsula and Petén Jungle.

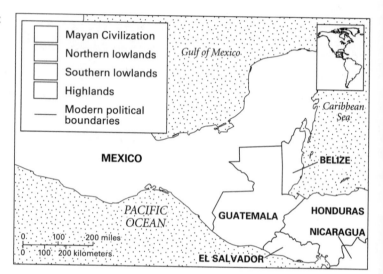

2. Draw a simple illustration or symbol for two achievements of the Olmecs. For each achievement, write one sentence explaining its importance.

3. On the timeline below, draw three horizontal bars and a label to show the span of years for each of the three main periods of Mayan civilization: Pre-Classic, Classic, and Post-Classic. Use a different color for each bar.

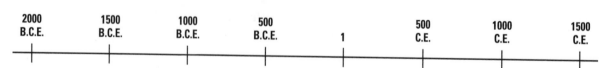

© Teachers' Curriculum Institute

Label each level in the pyramid below with the name of the appropriate Mayan social class. Inside the level for each social class, list at least three details about that group's duties, work, or lifestyle.

Imagine that this young Mayan man and woman are seeing each other for the first time.
Complete the thought bubbles by writing at least four more qualities that each hopes
the other possesses to make a good husband or wife. As you write your list of qualities,
think carefully about the typical tasks that Mayan women and men complete each day.

Add to the web below by listing at least two important pieces of information about each
Mayan religious belief or practice.

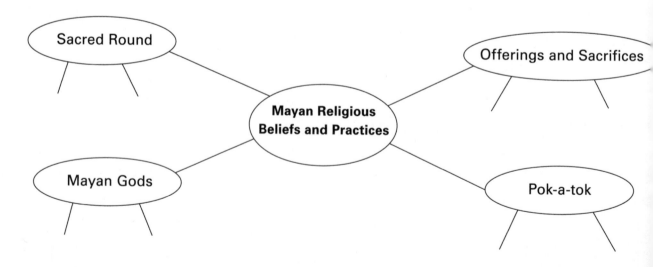

Section 22.6

In the three "fields" below the Temple of the Inscriptions in Palenque, do the following:

- In the first field, list three crops the Mayas planted.

- In the second field, draw and label pictures or describe three agricultural techniques used by the Mayas. Tell in what kind of environment each was used.

- In the third field, list three theories for the decline of the Mayan civilization. Circle the one you think was most responsible for the decline. Explain your choice.

Crops

Agricultural Techniques

Theories for Decline of the Mayan Civilization

PROCESSING

In each box below, design a new glyph, or symbol, to represent each aspect of Mayan culture. Label each of your glyphs, and write a short explanation of how it represents an important aspect of Mayan culture.

Class Structure

Explanation:

Family Life

Explanation:

Religious Beliefs and Practices

Explanation:

Agricultural Techniques

Explanation:

The Aztecs

How did the Aztecs rise to power?

This Aztec artwork contains clues about these three topics:

- the beginnings of the Aztec Empire
- the Aztec capital of Tenochtitlán
- the Aztecs' relations with their neighbors

Follow these steps.

1. Circle three details in the image. Each one should be a clue about each of the three topics above.

2. Near each detail you circled, write a note explaining what it tells about the topic.

3. Draw a line from each detail to its note.

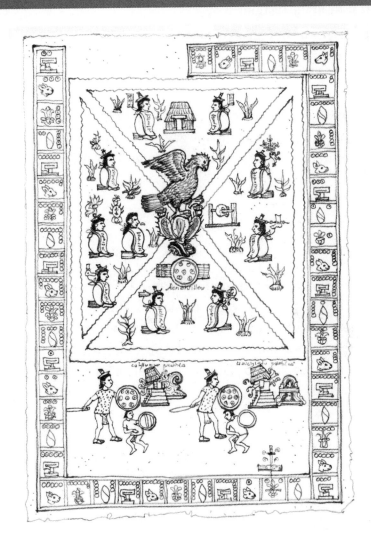

READING NOTES

Key Content Terms

As you complete the Reading Notes, use these terms in your answers.

Aztecs   Tenochtitlán   plaza   conformity

mercenary   alliance   causeway

Sections 23.2 to 23.4

Complete these steps for each section.

Step 1: Read the section.

Step 2: Record your answers to the questions in the space provided.

Step 3: Read the next section.

Section 23.2: The Aztecs in the Valley of Mexico

1. Name two important groups who lived in the Valley of Mexico before the Aztecs. Give an example of how each influenced the Aztecs.

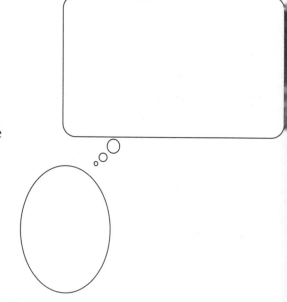

2. Draw the facial expression of a non-Aztec person already living in the Valley of Mexico when the Aztecs arrive. The expression should show how the person feels about the Aztecs. Then complete the thought bubble to explain how the person's group treated the Aztecs.

3. According to Aztec history, how did the Aztecs know where to build Tenochtitlán? Why did they think this was a good location?

Section 23.3: Tenochtitlán: A City of Wonders

1. At right, draw two architectural features
    the Aztecs used to allow them to build
    their capital in the middle of a lake. Label
    each feature.

2. Name at least one important building in Tenochtitlán, and describe its purpose.

3. Describe at least two aspects of Tenochtitlán that allowed so many people to live
    there comfortably.

Section 23.4: The Aztec Empire

1. What kinds of goods did the Aztecs receive in tribute from conquered peoples?
    Why was tribute so important to the Aztecs?

2. Complete the diagram below to show what happened before, during, and after
    an Aztec declaration of war.

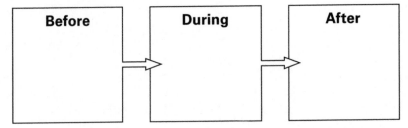

Before	During	After

3. What did the Aztecs demand of the peoples they conquered? Name one advantage
    and one disadvantage of this Aztec policy.

In the space below, design a flag for the Aztec Empire. Your flag should include these items.

- at least one symbol that represents something important about the arrival of the Aztecs in the Valley of Mexico
- at least one symbol that represents something important about their capital city of Tenochtitlán
- at least one symbol that represents something important about how they conquered and ruled their neighbors
- a variety of colors
- no more than five words

Daily Life in Tenochtitlán

What was daily life like for Aztecs in Tenochtitlán?

Analyze the section of the mural *The Great Market of Tenochtitlán* by Mexican artist Diego Rivera, which your teacher is projecting. Follow the directions, below. Then discuss the questions with your partner, and record your answers.

1. In the spaces below, quickly sketch five of the most interesting or important details you see in the mural.

2. What seems to be happening in this market? List at least three things you notice.

3. Based on this painting, what is at least one thing you can tell about the daily life of Aztecs in Tenochtitlán?

READING NOTES

Key Content Terms

As you complete the Reading Notes, use these terms in your answers.

semidivine   hereditary   ward   polygamy

Section 24.2

For each of the five classes in Aztec society on this page, list two important responsibilities or privileges of the class, and draw a simple symbol or illustration to represent the class.

Ruler

•

•

Government Officials, Priests, and Military Leaders

•

•

Commoners

•

•

Peasants

•

•

Slaves

•

•

Your teacher will assign three aspects of daily life in Tenochtitlán for you to research. Follow these three steps for each one:

1. Carefully read the corresponding section of the chapter.

2. List three important characteristics you learned about that aspect of daily life.

3. Look at the image of the Great Market and identify an item that represents each aspect of daily life. In the appropriate rectangle, create a simple, colorful drawing of the item and a simple label. (For example, for "Food" you might draw a purple squash or yellow corn tortillas.)

Section 24.3: Marriage
Three important characteristics of this aspect of Aztec daily life are

-
-
-

Section 24.4: Family Life
Three important characteristics of this aspect of Aztec daily life are

-
-
-

Section 24.5: Food

Three important characteristics of this aspect
of Aztec daily life are

*

*

*

Section 24.6: Markets

Three important characteristics of this aspect
of Aztec daily life are

*

*

*

Section 24.7: Religious Practices

Three important characteristics of this aspect
of Aztec daily life are

•

•

•

Section 24.8: Recreation

Three important characteristics of this aspect
of Aztec daily life are

•

•

•

PROCESSING

Suppose that you are an Aztec teenager visiting relatives in Tenochtitlán. This is the first time you have visited them, and today they took you to the Great Market. On the notebook page below, create a three-paragraph journal entry in which you describe what you saw and what you learned about how Aztecs live in Tenochtitlán. You should include information on at least three aspects of daily life that you learned about in this chapter.

The Incas

How did the Incas manage their large and remote empire?

PREVIEW

Carefully analyze the image your teacher is projecting, and answer these questions:

- What details do you see in this image?

- What do you notice about the physical geography of this setting?

- What might be some advantages to an empire with geography like this? What might be some disadvantages?

- Suppose you are the leader of the Inca Empire at its height, around 1500. The empire extends more than a thousand miles north and south of your capital. What kind of communication system might you set up to get important information to and from the far corners of your empire?

Key Content Terms

As you complete the Reading Notes, use these terms in your answers.

Incas   communal

ayllu   oracle

Section 25.2

1. Which present-day South American countries did the Inca Empire include?

2. Choose the two ideas the Incas adopted from each earlier culture (the
    Moches and the Chimus) that you think were the most important for the
    Incas in managing their empire. In the space below, draw a quick illustration
    or symbol for each idea, and write a sentence explaining why that idea was
    important to the Incas' ability to manage their empire.

Moches   **Chimus**

3. What physical obstacles did the Incas face in managing their empire? List at
    least three ways they overcame these obstacles.

Section 25.3

1. Who held the top position in the Incan class structure? From whom did the Incas believe he received his authority to rule?

2. Who were the Capac Incas? What jobs did they do?

3. Who were the curacas? What were some of their responsibilities?

4. To what class did most people in the Inca Empire belong? What kind of work did they do?

Section 25.4

1. Who owned the land each ayllu used? What did the ayllu members do on this land?

2. What was the mit'a? How was it paid?

3. How was the education of the sons of Incan nobles different from that of children of commoners?

4. At what ages did Incan men and women marry? What were the typical steps people followed to find a partner and get married?

Section 25.5

1. Which god was the most important to the Incas? Why?

2. Describe the types of sacrifices the Incas practiced in their religious ceremonies.

3. How old were girls who were selected to become Chosen Women? What did they learn to do in the convents?

4. What could happen to Chosen Women after age 15?

Section 25.6

1. What did the Sapa Inca do first when he wanted to include a new group in his empire? Why did he use this strategy?

2. What happened to groups that resisted inclusion in the Inca Empire?

3. What things did the leaders of groups that became part of the Inca Empire have to do?

4. What unique belief did the Incas have about the lands conquered by the Sapa Inca? How may this have led the Incas to conquer such a large empire?

PROCESSING

Follow these steps to fill in the Venn diagrams on this page and the next page.

1. Select two of these topics: class structure, family life, religion, or relations with other peoples.

2. Write the name of each topic on the line above each Venn diagram.

3. Where the ovals overlap in the diagrams, list two things the Incan civilization has in common with your own society.

4. In each part where the ovals do not overlap, list two things that differ between the Incas and your own society.

Topic: _____

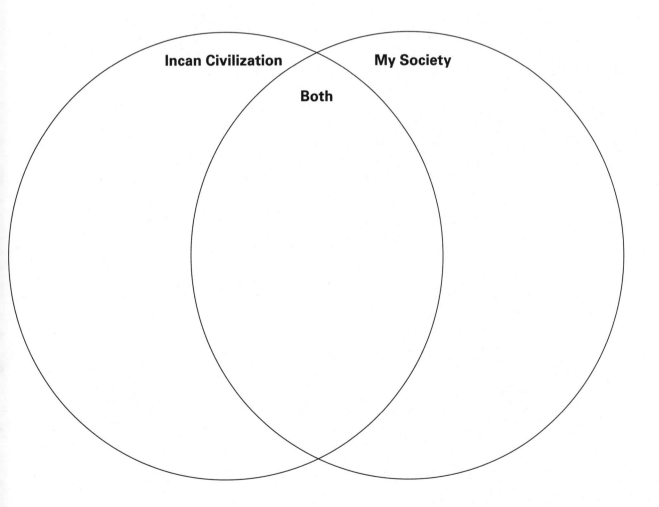

Topic: _____

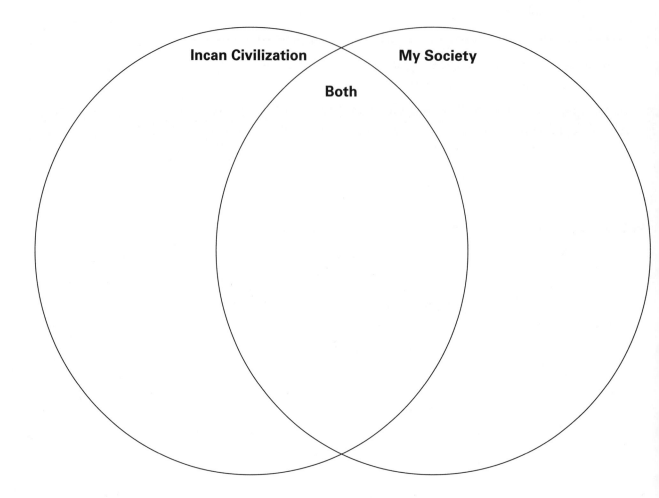

Incan Civilization

My Society

Both

Achievements of the Mayas, Aztecs, and Incas

What were the significant achievements of the Mayas, Aztecs, and Incas?

PREVIEW

Think of important achievements or advances of the last 50 years. Consider achievements in such areas as science, technology, the arts, and communication. In the space below, do the following:

- Draw a symbol for at least two of these achievements.
- Label each symbol with the name of the achievement it represents.
- Near each symbol, write a sentence that answers this question: Do you think this achievement will still be used by people 500 to 1,000 years from now? Why or why not?

READING NOTES

Key Content Terms

As you complete the Reading Notes, use these terms in your answers.

| solar year | glyph | pictograph | trephination |
| stele | dialect | suspension bridge | |

If you are doing the activity, complete all questions in the the Reading Notes.
(Note: If you are not doing the activity, skip Part 2 for each section.)

Section 26.2

Part 1: Mayan Achievements

Read Section 26.2 and record at least two examples of Mayan achievements in each area listed below. Explain why the examples you chose were significant.

Science and technology:

Arts and architecture:

Language and writing:

Part 2: Mayan Artifacts

Examine the materials at each station, and identify four artifacts related to the Mayan civilization. Then write the artifact letter, the placard letter, and label each artifact in the space provided. If appropriate, make a quick sketch of the artifact in the museum "display cases" below.

Artifact _____ on Placard _____
is _____

Artifact _____ on Placard _____
is _____

Artifact _____ on Placard _____
is _____

Artifact _____ on Placard _____
is _____

Part 1: Aztec Achievements

Read Section 26.3 and record at least two examples of Aztec achievements in each area listed below. Explain why the examples you chose were significant.

Science and technology:

Arts and architecture:

Language and writing:

Part 2: Aztec Artifacts

Examine the materials at each station, and identify four artifacts related to the Aztec civilization. Then write the artifact letter, the placard letter, and label each artifact in the space provided. If appropriate, make a quick sketch of the artifact in the museum "display cases" below.

Artifact _____ on Placard _____
is _____

Artifact _____ on Placard _____
is _____

Artifact _____ on Placard _____
is _____

Artifact _____ on Placard _____
is _____

Part 1: Incan Achievements

Read Section 26.4 and record at least two examples of Incan achievements in each area listed below. Explain why the examples you chose were significant.

Science and technology:

Arts and architecture:

Language and writing:

Part 2: Incan Artifacts

Examine the materials at each station, and identify four artifacts related to the Incan civilization. Then write the artifact letter, the placard letter, and label each artifact in the space provided. If appropriate, make a quick sketch of the artifact in the museum "display cases" below.

Artifact _____ on Placard _____

is _____

Artifact _____ on Placard _____

is _____

Artifact _____ on Placard _____

is _____

Artifact _____ on Placard _____

is _____

PROCESSING

In the space below, design and create a planning sketch for a mosaic about Mayan, Aztec, and Incan achievements for your museum's courtyard. A mosaic is made of odd-shaped fragments, often colored tile or glass. Your mosaic should have at least nine fragments—three for each civilization—which you can make from odd-shaped pieces of construction paper or other similar materials fitted together. Each fragment should include the following:

- a creative and colorful visual symbol to represent one of the important achievements of the Mayas, Aztecs, or Incas

- a short label that identifies the achievement

- color-coding to identify the civilization responsible for the achievement. Achievements for the same civilization should be coded the same color

Then, attach your final mosaic design on the next page.

Achievements of the Mayas, Aztecs, and Incas **195**

Mosaic of Achievements

Preparing to Write: Categorizing Information

Suppose you are a tour guide. You want to take a group to Peru to watch the rebuilding of the Apurimac rope bridge. The chart below lists the types of visitors you want to attract. For each type, list three reasons why he or she might want to sign up for the trip. For example, a scientist might go to learn how the bridge is made.

Reasons to Sign Up for the Trip	
Historian	
Scientist	
Tourist	

Now list objections each type of visitor might have to signing up for the trip. For example, a tourist might say it is too dangerous for his or her children.

Objections to Signing Up for the Trip	
Historian	
Scientist	
Tourist	

Writing Persuasive Paragraphs

Choose one type of visitor from the charts on the previous page. Write two paragraphs to persuade this person to join your tour. In the first paragraph, give reasons why the person should make the trip. In the second paragraph, offer arguments against the person's objections. Use the completed charts to help you. Be persuasive. Start your paragraphs with a strong, interesting topic sentence.

Use this rubric to evaluate your paragraphs. Make changes to your paragraphs if you need to.

Score	Description
3	The paragraphs have a strong topic sentence. The first paragraph presents convincing reasons why the person should join the trip. The second paragraph offers clear arguments against the objections. There are no spelling or grammar errors.
2	The paragraphs have a topic sentence. The first paragraph presents reasons why the person should join the trip. The second paragraph offers arguments against the objections. There are some spelling or grammatical errors.
1	The paragraphs lack a topic sentence. The first paragraph lacks convincing reasons why the person should join the trip. The second paragraph lacks arguments against the objections. There are many spelling or grammar errors.

Timeline Skills

Analyze the Unit 6 timeline in your book. Also think about what you have learned in this unit. Then answer the following questions.

1. For about how many years did the Mayan civilization last?

2. During what period of Mayan civilization were their hieroglyphics developed?

3. What are two of the cultural achievements that occurred during the Classic period of Mayan civilization?

4. How many years passed between the Incas settling in Cuzco and beginning to expand their empire?

5. What was unusual about the location and construction of Tenochtitlán?

6. Why did the Aztec Empire have many enemies?

7. How did the Incas expand their empire so rapidly after 1438?

8. What two things did the Incas build to help them manage their empire?

9. During what century did the Spanish defeat the Aztec and Inca empires?

Critical Thinking

Use the timeline and the chapters in the unit to answer the following questions.

10. Historians have proposed many theories about what caused the end of Mayan civilization. In one sentence each, summarize the four theories you learned in this unit. Circle the one you think is most likely. Add a sentence explaining your reasoning.

11. How did the Aztec Empire expand? In your answer, describe the Aztecs' policies toward conquered groups and the challenges the Aztecs faced.

12. How did the Incas control their large empire? In your answer, describe the main challenge the Incas faced and some of the innovations they used to help them manage such a large area.

13. If you could add two more events to this timeline, which would they be? List each event, and explain why you think it is important enough to add to the timeline.

    a.

    b.

Europe's Renaissance and Reformation

Geography Challenge

Timeline Challenge

Europe, About 1500

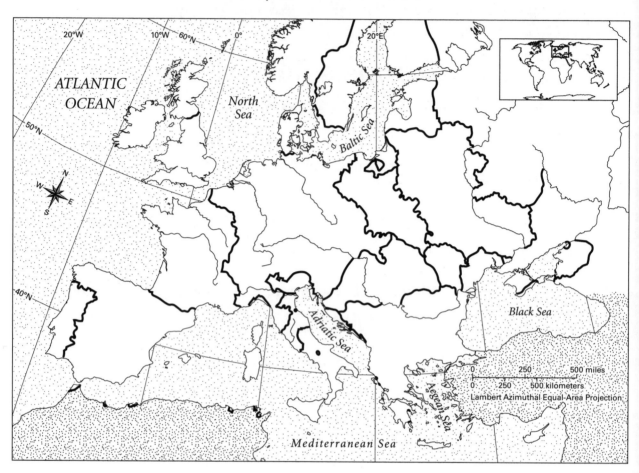

Geography Skills

Analyze the maps in "Setting the Stage" for Unit 7 in your book. Then answer the following questions and fill out the map as directed.

1. Locate the following cities and label them on your map: Venice, Florence, Milan, Madrid, Paris, London, Worms, Wittenberg.

2. Locate the Holy Roman Empire. Shade it green on your map and label it.

3. Locate the Papal States. Shade them red and label them. Label Rome.

4. Locate the following countries on your map: Spain, France, and England. Shade each a different color and label it. Which of these is an island nation?

5. Locate the city of Avignon. Label it on your map. In what country is it located?

6. Label the Elbe River, Rhine River, and Danube River.

7. The city-state of Venice is located on what body of water?

8. Based on location, which city in western Europe was most likely a center of trade with Africa and Asia? Why?

Critical Thinking

Answer the following questions in complete sentences.

9. Locate the city of Wittenberg. A major religious movement began in Wittenberg and spread through Europe. What physical feature might have helped this movement spread from Wittenberg?

10. For centuries, the pope had been based in Rome. Then, in 1309, Pope Clement V moved the Roman Catholic Church to Avignon, France. Given the power of the Church at that time, how might this move have affected the relationship between the Church and the Papal States? Between the Church and the Italian city-states? How might it have affected France?

The Renaissance Begins

What changes in Europe led to the Renaissance?

Examine the diagram at right. Then answer the following questions *on a separate piece of paper.*

1. In this "Renaissance plant," which root grows straight up? Which roots branch out? What might this tell us about how the two time periods—medieval and classical—influenced the growth of the Renaissance?

2. Plants need soil, sunlight, and water to grow. In the diagram, what three things seem to be contributing to the growth of the Renaissance?

3. Why do you think that the soil is labeled "Europe"?

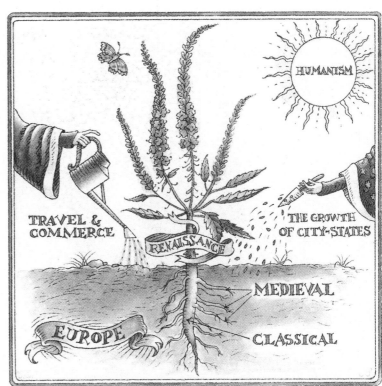

Key Content Terms

As you complete the Reading Notes, use these terms in your answers.

Renaissance	republic	individualism
classical art	humanism	
city-state	humanities	

If your class is doing the activity for this chapter, complete all parts of the Reading Notes for Section 27.2. *(Note: If your class is not doing the activity, skip Part 3 for this section.)*

Part 1

1. Fill in the cause-and-effect chart below to explain how the classical world of ancient Greece and Rome was rediscovered, leading to the period known as the Renaissance.

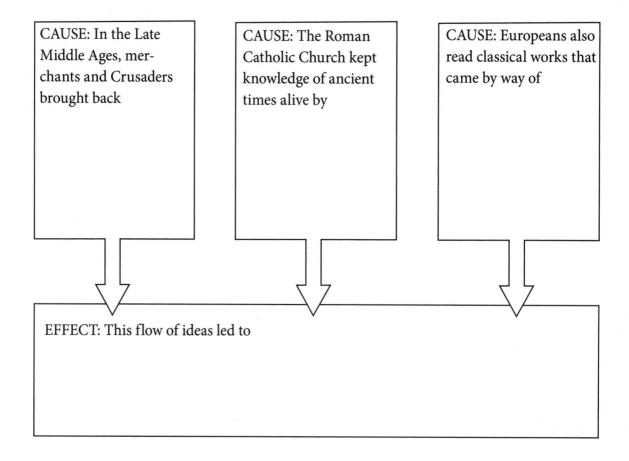

CAUSE: In the Late Middle Ages, merchants and Crusaders brought back

CAUSE: The Roman Catholic Church kept knowledge of ancient times alive by

CAUSE: Europeans also read classical works that came by way of

EFFECT: This flow of ideas led to

Part 2

As you read the subsection in your book entitled "Exploring the Rebirth of Classical Ideas Through Art," fill in the first two rows of the matrix below.

	Classical	Medieval	Renaissance
Purpose of this type of art			
Two style characteristics of each example in your book			

Part 3

Once your teacher projects Visual 27B, examine the three images and fill in the this chart by doing the following.

- Decide in which period each artwork was created. Write the period and letter of each work in the correct row.
- List two or more characteristics from Section 27.2 that led you to your decision.

Letter identifying the artwork			
Two or three style characteristics in this piece of art			

This fishbone diagram is used to show several causes for one effect. Follow the directions in the last question for each section to complete this diagram about some different events or developments that led to the start of the Renaissance.

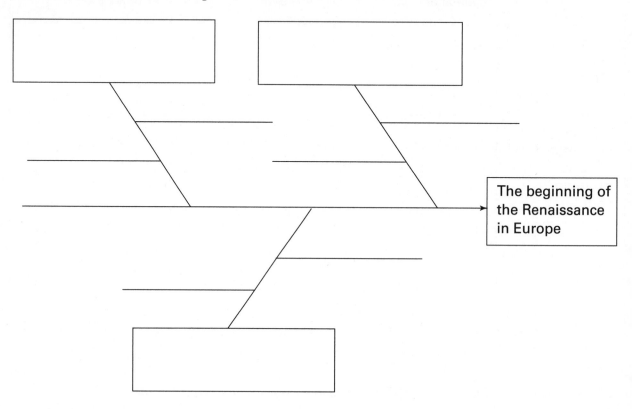

The beginning of the Renaissance in Europe

Section 27.3

1. Describe how Marco Polo's travels along the Silk Road helped reawaken interest in classical culture.

2. List and explain two results of the increase in trade in Europe.

3. Identify the primary factor from this section that led to the start of the Renaissance. In one of the large rectangles in the fishbone diagram above, write this factor. Then, on the lines below the rectangle, provide at least two supporting details that further explain how this led to the rebirth of classical culture and learning in Europe.

Section 27.4

1. What were Italian city-states? How were they governed?

2. How did Italian city-states become so powerful?

3. Identify the primary factor from this section that led to the start of the Renaissance. In a second rectangle in the fishbone diagram on the previous page, write this factor. Then, on the lines below the rectangle, provide at least two supporting details that further explain how this led to the rebirth of classical culture and learning in Europe.

Section 27.5

1. What did Renaissance humanists believe about people's abilities?

2. What subjects from ancient times did humanists study and explore?

3. How did the Renaissance humanists' beliefs sometimes conflict with those of the Catholic Church?

4. Identify the primary factor from this section that led to the start of the Renaissance. In the last rectangle in the fishbone diagram on the previous page, write this factor. Then, on the lines below the rectangle, provide at least two supporting details that further explain how this led to the rebirth of classical culture and learning in Europe.

Write a paragraph explaining the illustration below. Describe what it shows about changes in European life at the end of the Middle Ages that led to the flowering of arts and learning called the Renaissance. Include the following words in your explanation: *trade, banking, towns, city-states, classical, humanism.*

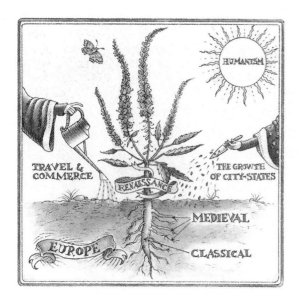

Florence: The Cradle of the Renaissance

What advances were made during the Renaissance?

Examine the photograph of Florence. Then circle five key features or structures and write a sentence about what each one might tell you about the city. For example, you might circle a mountain in the background and say that mountains indicate that Florence is in a valley.

READING NOTES

Key Content Terms

As you complete the Reading Notes, use these terms in your answers.

Florence	secular	Niccolò Machiavelli
Donatello	Dante Alighieri	
Michelangelo	Leonardo da Vinci	

Section 28.2

1. What factors helped Florence to become a wealthy city?

2. How did Florence's wealth contribute to its cultural activity?

3. Why did many travelers come to Florence?

If your class is doing the activity for this chapter, complete all the Reading Notes for each section. *(Note: If your class is not doing the activity, skip Question 3 under each section.)*

Section 28.3

1. How were architects and builders of the Renaissance influenced by both classical and humanist ideas?

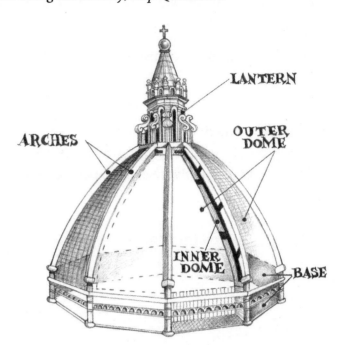

2. How did Brunelleschi build a dome that would not collapse?

3. Compare your human dome to Brunelleschi's dome by completing the sentences.

- On our dome, the parts of our bodies that supported the most weight were

- On Brunelleschi's dome, the parts that supported the most weight were

- The feet on our dome were like the _____ on Brunelleschi's dome.
- The beach ball on our dome was like the _____ on Brunelleschi's dome.
- The bodies on our dome were like the _____ on Brunelleschi's dome.

Section 28.4

1. Briefly describe how classical cultures and humanism influenced Renaissance painters.

2. Briefly describe two Renaissance advances in painting techniques.

3. Botticelli painted *Adoration of the Magi* in about 1482. In the left column of the chart below, list at least two details from the image. In the right column, identify the perspective technique Botticelli used for each. An example has been provided.

Detail from Image	Perspective Technique
People	The figures close to the viewer seem bigger; those farther away seem smaller

Section 28.5

1. How were Renaissance sculptors influenced by humanist ideals and ancient Roman statues?

2. What is significant about Donatello's *David?* About Michelangelo's *David?*

3. What was it like to try to sculpt an eye? What do you think it might have been like for Michelangelo to create his *David* from a block of marble?

Section 28.6

1. Briefly describe two ways in which Renaissance literature differed from medieval literature.

2. How is Dante's *The Divine Comedy* an example of humanist art?

3. Write the part of *The Divine Comedy*—*Inferno, Purgatorio,* or *Paradiso*—that each image on Placard 28D illustrates.

   Image A:

   Image B:

   Image C:

Section 28.7

1. How did the study of science change during the Renaissance?

2. Quickly sketch and label three items that represent different science or mathematics topics Leonardo da Vinci explored in his notebooks.

3. Write what you think each drawing by Leonardo da Vinci on Placard 28E represents, using the list on Station Materials 28A.

   Drawing A:

   Drawing B:

   Drawing C:

   Drawing D:

Section 28.8

1. How did the Medici family influence and rule in Renaissance Florence?

2. What did Machiavelli write about in *The Prince?* How did this book contradict humanist ideals? In what ways was it a very modern work?

3. Rewrite each quotation from *The Prince* below in your own words.

   Quotation 1: "A prince should have no other aim or thought, nor take up any other thing for his study, but war and its organization and discipline, for that is the only art that is necessary to one who commands."

   My interpretation:

   Quotation 2: "Thus, it is well to seem merciful, faithful, humane, sincere, religious, and also to be so; but you must have the mind so disposed [ready] that when it is merciful to be otherwise, you may be able to change to the opposite qualities."

   My interpretation:

   Quotation 3: "In the actions of men, and especially of princes, from which there is no appeal, the end justifies the means."

   My interpretation:

Section 28.9

1. What industries helped Florence become the center of the Renaissance?

2. What were two differences between Florence's Old Market and New Market?

3. In the chart below, list the item(s) you purchased with your florins. Complete each column by entering the price and the number of florins remaining. Remember that you have 15 florins. You must have a zero balance in the third column when you are done.

Item	Price in Florins	Florins Remaining

Use your Reading Notes to create a scrapbook page about what you learned about Renaissance Florence. Follow these steps to create your scrapbook page.

1. Write a caption for each image below that explains what it shows and tells about Florence.

2. *On a separate sheet of paper,* write a paragraph that describes Florence at the time of the Renaissance. Use precise, descriptive words to create a visual image in the reader's mind.

My Scrapbook Page of Renaissance Florence

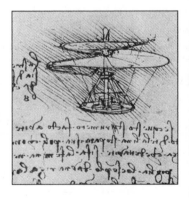

Leading Figures of the Renaissance

In what ways have various leading figures of the Renaissance affected modern society?

PREVIEW

Choose a political leader, artist, entertainer, or other well-known figure who you think has been influential in the period from 1900 to the present day. A list of suggestions has been provided below, or you can choose someone else who fits one of the categories. Then, *on a separate sheet of paper,* do the following:

• Briefly describe the person and why you chose him or her.

• Name at least three of the person's talents, accomplishments, or achievements.

• Explain why he or she has been influential.

Leaders

Franklin D. Roosevelt

Mahatma Gandhi

Ronald Reagan

Bill Clinton

Artists and Entertainers

Oprah Winfrey

The Beatles

Elvis Presley

J.K. Rowling

Inventors, Scientists, and Business Persons

Henry Ford

Bill Gates

Walt Disney

Jonas Salk

Albert Einstein

Heroes and Icons

Mother Teresa

Neil Armstrong

Martin Luther King, Jr.

Pope John Paul II

READING NOTES

Key Content Terms

As you complete the Reading Notes, use these terms in your answers.

Johannes Gutenberg   William Shakespeare

New World   Miguel Cervantes

Section 29.2

1. How did Renaissance ideas spread from Italy to the rest of Europe?

2. How did Gutenberg's printing press improve upon existing printing methods?

3. How did the printing press help to spread new ideas, discoveries, and inventions?

Sections 29.3 to 29.12

If your class is doing the activity for this chapter, complete all the Reading Notes for each section. *(Note: If your class is not doing the activity, skip Question 2 under each section.)*

Section 29.3

1. Name:

    Title (from section title):

    Lived (years of birth and death):

    From (the place):

    Personality and Training:

    Talents and Achievements:

2. I think Pedestal _____ represents this figure because

Section 29.4

1. Name:

    Title (from section title):

    Lived (years of birth and death):

    From (the place):

    Personality and Training:

    Talents and Achievements:

2. I think Pedestal _____ represents this figure because

Section 29.5

1. Name:

   Title (from section title):

   Lived (years of birth and death):

   From (the place):

   Personality and Training:

   Talents and Achievements:

2. I think Pedestal _____ represents this figure because

Section 29.6

1. Name:

   Title (from section title):

   Lived (years of birth and death):

   From (the place):

   Personality and Training:

   Talents and Achievements:

2. I think Pedestal _____ represents this figure because

Section 29.7

1. Name:

    Title (from section title):

    Lived (years of birth and death):

    From (the place):

    Personality and Training:

    Talents and Achievements:

2. I think Pedestal _____ represents this figure because

Section 29.8

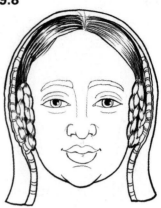

1. Name:

    Title (from section title):

    Lived (years of birth and death):

    From (the place):

    Personality and Training:

    Talents and Achievements:

2. I think Pedestal _____ represents this figure because

Section 29.9

Section 29.10

1. Name:

    Title (from section title):

    Lived (years of birth and death):

    From (the place):

    Personality and Training:

    Talents and Achievements:

2. I think Pedestal _____ represents this figure because

1. Name:

    Title (from section title):

    Lived (years of birth and death):

    From (the place):

    Personality and Training:

    Talents and Achievements:

2. I think Pedestal _____ represents this figure because

Section 29.11

1. Name:

   Title (from section title):

   Lived (years of birth and death):

   From (the place):

   Personality and Training:

   Talents and Achievements:

2. I think Pedestal _____ represents this
   figure because

Section 29.12

1. Name:

   Title (from section title):

   Lived (years of birth and death):

   From (the place):

   Personality and Training:

   Talents and Achievements:

2. I think Pedestal _____ represents this
   figure because

PROCESSING

You are hosting a dinner party for leading Renaissance figures. The guest list will include the ten figures you learned about in this chapter. Your goal is for all your guests to enjoy lively conversation throughout a Renaissance feast.

You must decide where your guests will sit. As you decide where to place each guest, consider what you know about his or her language, personality, training, talents, and achievements so that everyone has something to talk about with nearby guests at the table.

On a separate sheet of paper, copy the drawing below. At each chair, create a place card that has the guest's name, or sketch the face, and write his or her title from the section title in the book. Leave space around the table to write one or two sentences that answer the following question for each guest: *Why did you seat this person where you did?*

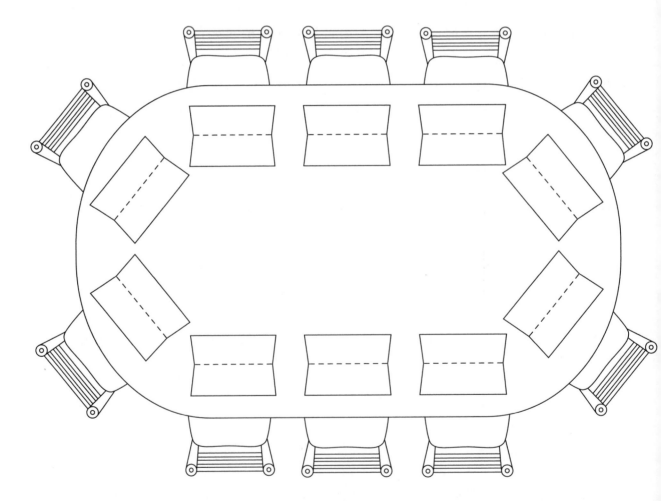

Preparing to Write: Developing an Argument and Supporting Details

Which do you think is a better form of communication—print media, such as books and newspapers, or the Internet? What are the strengths of each? What are the weaknesses of each?

	Strengths	Weaknesses
Print Media		
Internet		

Decide whether you will persuade your readers that print media or the Internet is a superior form of communication. Write a position statement that gives your overall opinion here.

List at least four details that support your opinion. The details should consist of logical reasons, facts, examples, and personal experiences.

1.

2.

3.

4.

Writing a Persuasive Paragraph

Now use your thinking from the previous page to write a persuasive paragraph.
Begin with your position statement. Then present each of your supporting details
in full sentences, in a clear and logical way.

Use this rubric to evaluate your persuasive paragraph. Make changes in your
paragraph if you need to.

Score	Description
3	The paragraph has a direct and forceful position statement. It includes excellent supporting details, including logical reasons, facts, examples, and personal experience. The paragraph is logically organized. There are no errors in spelling or grammar.
2	The paragraph has a satisfactory position statement. It includes good supporting details, including some logical reasons, facts, examples, and personal experience. The paragraph is adequately organized. There are some errors in spelling or grammar.
1	The paragraph lacks a position statement. It includes few supporting details. The paragraph is poorly and illogically organized. There are many errors in spelling or grammar.

The Reformation Begins

What factors led to the weakening of the Catholic Church and the beginning of the Reformation?

Your school's principal has just enacted a policy regarding dress code violations that you believe unfairly targets certain students. You would like to voice your opinion, but are concerned that doing so might label you a troublemaker. Which of the following courses of action should you take?

A. Ask for an appointment with the principal and explain your concerns about the policy face to face.

B. Create a pamphlet that outlines your arguments against the new policy and pass it out to students at lunchtime.

C. Stand on the sidewalk outside the school and, as students leave school for the day, protest loudly against the new policy.

D. Ask your parents if you can transfer to another school where you know the dress code policy is fairer.

E. Stay quiet and wait to see if other students are also upset before you start speaking out against the policy.

Now, in a few sentences, explain why you chose that particular course of action.

Key Content Terms

As you complete the Reading Notes, use these terms in your answers.

indulgence	Reformation	Martin Luther
simony	Protestant	denomination

Section 30.2

1. Complete the chart below by identifying three similarities between the classroom activity and the Catholic Church's selling of indulgences.

Classroom Activity	Historical Connection
• The school attempted to raise money by selling points to students.	•
• Students who performed poorly on the quiz or other assignments were told they could still earn high grades by buying points.	•
• Students who honored the academic process or couldn't afford to buy points were troubled by the policy, believing it was wrong or unfair.	•

2. Name three factors, besides selling indulgences, that contributed to the weakening of the Catholic Church.

   a.

   b.

   c.

1. What teachings and actions of John Wycliffe led the pope to accuse him of heresy?

2. What reforms did Jan Hus call for?

3. In what way did Catherine of Siena's approach to faith help prepare people for the Reformation?

4. Who was Desiderius Erasmus? How did he help to prepare Europe for the Reformation?

Section 30.4

1. Why did Martin Luther write the Ninety-Five Theses and post them on the door of a church in Wittenberg?

2. Use this chart to compare and contrast Luther's beliefs with those of the Catholic Church.

Martin Luther	Catholic Church

3. What happened when Luther was brought before the Diet of Worms?

1. Name three factors that helped spread Luther's reforms across Europe.

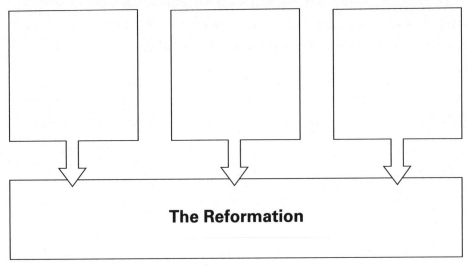

The Reformation

2. What two Protestant reformers began new churches in Switzerland?

3. What personal and political reasons led King Henry VIII to split with the Catholic Church?

Personal Reasons	Political Reasons

4. Who was William Tyndale? For what important contribution is he most remembered?

In each outline, draw facial features to show how each of these six individuals felt about the need to reform the Catholic Church. Then, under each head, complete the sentence to express what each person would say about the Reformation. An example is provided.

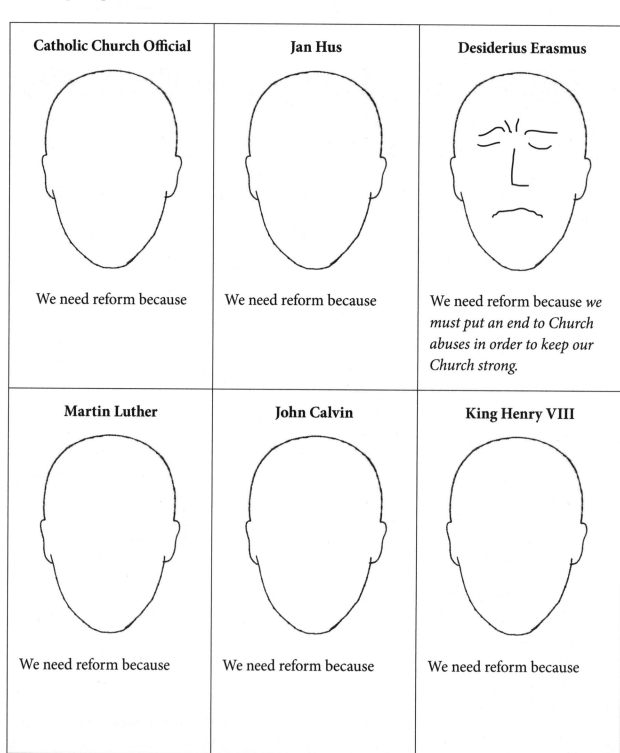

Catholic Church Official

We need reform because

Jan Hus

We need reform because

Desiderius Erasmus

We need reform because *we must put an end to Church abuses in order to keep our Church strong.*

Martin Luther

We need reform because

John Calvin

We need reform because

King Henry VIII

We need reform because

The Spread and Impact of the Reformation

What were the effects of the Reformation?

PREVIEW

This diagram shows some of the main branches of Christianity today. Answer the questions below about the diagram *on a separate sheet of a paper.*

1. What do you see?

2. What are the three main branches of Christianity?

3. Why do you think all the branches are considered part of Christianity?

4. Find Lutheranism, Calvinism, and Anglicanism on the diagram. To which larger branch do they belong?

5. Have you seen examples of these different forms of Christianity in your community? In what ways?

6. How do you think Catholic leaders may have reacted to the growing number of Protestant churches in the 15th and 16th centuries?

Eastern Orthodox

Roman Catholic

Christianity

Anglican

 Episcopal

 United Church of Christ

 Methodist

 Pentecostal Assembly

 Church of God

Calvinist

 Baptist

 Church of Christ

 Presbyterian

 Reformed

 Society of Friends (Quakers)

Protestant

Lutheran

Anabaptist

 Mennonite

 Amish

Latter-Day Saints

Adventist

Christian Scientist

Unitarian Universalist

Key Content Terms

As you complete the Reading Notes, use these terms in your answers.

Lutheranism	Anglicanism	absolute monarchy
Calvinism	Counter-Reformation	Puritans
theocracy	nationalism	

Sections 31.2 to 31.4

Read Sections 31.2 through 31.4. In the corresponding part of the matrix below and on the next page, for each denomination of Christianity, record at least two key ideas about each topic. Then, use a highlighter or marker to highlight details that are similar for each denomination in the matrix, using the same color.

	Lutheranism	Calvinism	Anglicanism
Origins of the Denomination			
Beliefs About Sin and Salvation			

	Lutheranism	Calvinism	Anglicanism
Beliefs About the Ultimate Source of Authority			
Rituals and Worship			
Community Life			

1. What was the Council of Trent? What did the council do?

2. What was the Society of Jesus?

3. How did the Society of Jesus help strengthen the Catholic Church?

4. What else did the Catholic Church do to stop the spread of Protestantism?

1. On the map, use two different colors to shade in the major Protestant areas and those that were Catholic. Create a map key to explain your shading.

Religious Divisions in Europe

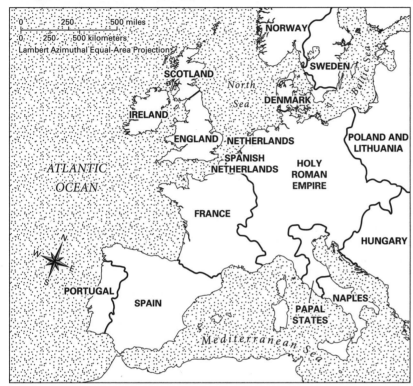

2. How did the Reformation plant seeds of democratic ideas?

3. In the chart below, list areas where Catholic and Protestant missionaries traveled after the Reformation and the Counter-Reformation.

Areas of the World Where Catholic Missionaries Traveled	Areas of the World Where Protestant Missionaries Traveled

PROCESSING

Complete the Venn diagram to show the key differences and similarities between Catholic and Protestant churches during the Reformation. List similarities in the overlapping part of the ovals and differences in the parts that do not overlap. Use the list below to guide you.

- origins
- beliefs about sin and salvation
- beliefs about the ultimate source of authority
- rituals and worship
- community life

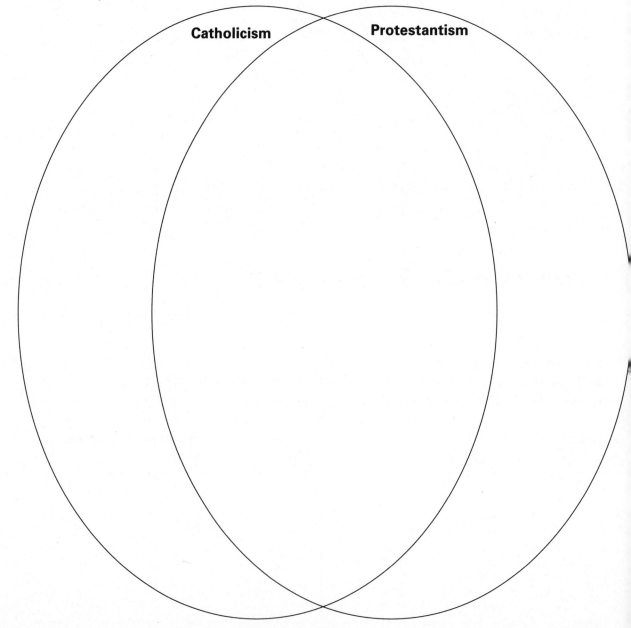

Timeline Skills

Analyze the Unit 7 timeline in your book. Also think about what you have learned in this unit. Then answer the following questions.

1. How was Brunelleschi able to complete the construction of the cathedral in Florence?

2. What did the pope's relocation of his headquarters to France signify to many Europeans?

3. What movement occurred in Europe from about the 1300s to the 1600s?

4. Why was Gutenberg's printing press significant?

5. How long did it take Michelangelo to sculpt *David*?

6. Name two events in the early 1500s that helped cause the Reformation.

7. What new denomination of Christianity was founded after the publication of *Institutes of the Christian Religion*?

8. What was the Council of Trent and what was its purpose?

9. What was one result of the Thirty Years' War?

Critical Thinking
Use the timeline and the chapters in the unit to answer the following questions.

10. Identify two ideals of humanists and explain how these ideals affected European thinking.

11. Choose two leading figures of the Renaissance and describe the advances each made in his or her field.

12. Choose two leading figures of the Reformation and explain their significance.

13. If you could add three more events to this timeline, which would they be? List each event, and explain why you think it is important enough to add to the timeline.

    a.

    b.

    c.

The Age of Exploration

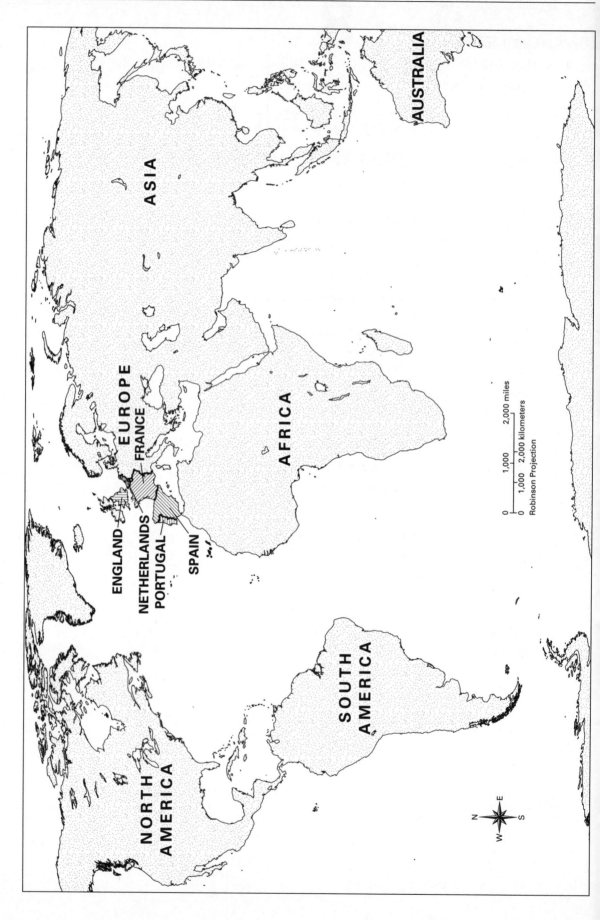

Geography Skills

Analyze the maps in "Setting the Stage" for Unit 8 in your book. Then answer the following questions and fill out the map as directed.

1. Label the Atlantic Ocean, the Pacific Ocean, and the Indian Ocean.

2. Da Gama was the first to find a sea route to Asia. He sailed for Portugal in 1497. Find his route on the map in your book. Then draw his route on your map. Label the route with his name.

3. Cabral was the first explorer to sail to the east coast of South America. He sailed for Portugal. Find his route on the map in your book. Then draw his route on your map. Label the route with his name.

4. By 1600, on which continents did Portugal claim or control territory or cities? On your map, shade the regions claimed by Portugal.

5. Columbus was the first explorer to sail to the Caribbean Islands. He sailed for Spain. Find his route on the map in your book. Then draw his route on your map. Label the route with his name.

6. Magellan was the first to lead a voyage that eventually went around the world. He sailed for Spain. Find his route on the map in your book. Then draw his route on your map. Label the route with his name.

7. Which European countries during this period sent explorers to North America's east coast?

Critical Thinking

Answer the following questions in complete sentences.

8. Describe the route that da Gama took to reach Asia. What does his route tell you about the possible reason why European monarchs wanted to find a different route to Asia?

9. Christopher Columbus sailed westward looking for a route to Asia. What does his expedition reveal about Europeans' knowledge of the world at that time?

10. Portugal was the first European country to send out explorers in the Age of Exploration. Why do you think this was so?

The Age of Exploration

How did the Age of Exploration change the way Europeans viewed the world?

PREVIEW

On a separate piece of paper, answer the following questions.

- What do you think motivates the United States to explore space today? Include two or three possible motives.

- Should the United States spend more or less money on the exploration of space? Give reasons for your answer.

READING NOTES

Key Content Terms

As you complete the Reading Notes, use these terms in your answers.

Age of Exploration	capitalism
cartography	market economy
colony	cottage industry
epidemic	mercantilism

Section 32.2

1. From your reading, choose three of the motives for exploration. Rank the motives in terms of how influential you think each was in causing the Age of Exploration.

   1st:

   2nd:

   3rd:

2. List four of the advances that allowed for easier exploration during this time. Then write a one-sentence explanation of each advance. An example is done for you.

   - Cartography: Improved mapmaking led to more accurate maps, which helped explorers by making navigation easier.

   •

   •

   •

1. On the map below, accurately draw the routes of Vasco da Gama and Pedro Cabral. Label each route with the last name of the explorer and the dates of his expedition.

Routes of Portuguese Explorations

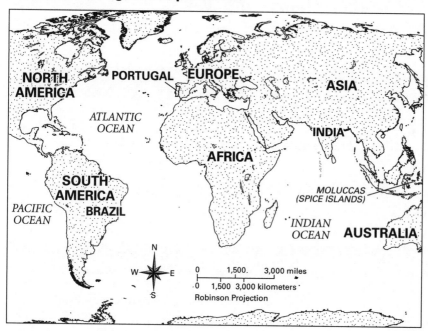

2. Complete the following sentences:

Vasco de Gama was important to Portuguese exploration because

Pedro Cabral was important to Portuguese exploration because

3. List the effects of Portuguese exploration. Your list should include at least five different effects. An example is done for you.

   • brought gold and slaves from Africa to Europe

   •

   •

   •

   •

1. On the map below, accurately draw in the routes of Christopher Columbus and Ferdinand Magellan. Label each route with the last name of the explorer and the dates of his expedition.

Routes of Early Spanish Explorations

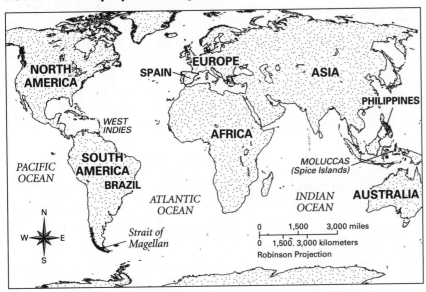

2. Complete the following sentences:

Christopher Columbus was important to Spanish exploration because

Ferdinand Magellan was important to Spanish exploration because

3. List the various effects of early Spanish exploration. Your list should include at least five different effects. An example is done for you.
   • revealed the existence of the Americas, a "New World" to Europeans
   •
   •
   •
   •

1. On the map below, accurately draw in the routes of Hernán Cortés and Francisco Pizarro. Label each route with the last name of the explorer and the dates of his expedition.

Routes of Later Spanish Explorations

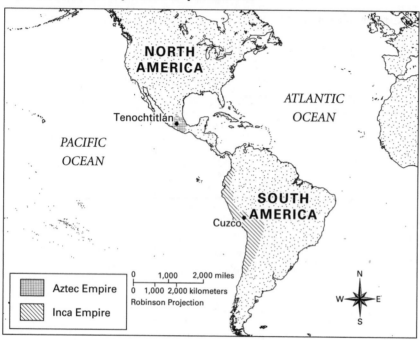

2. Complete the following sentences:

   Hernán Cortés was important to Spanish exploration because

   Francisco Pizarro was important to Spanish exploration because

3. List the various effects of later Spanish exploration. Your list should include at least five different effects. An example is done for you.

   • rapidly expanded Spain's foreign trade and overseas colonization

   •

   •

   •

   •

1. On the map below, accurately draw in the routes of John Cabot, Giovanni da Verrazano, and Henry Hudson. Label each route with the last name of the explorer and the dates of his expedition.

Routes of Other European Explorations

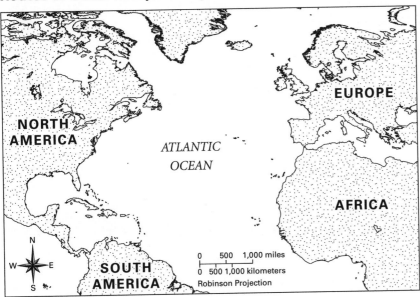

2. Complete the following sentences:

   John Cabot was important to English exploration because

   Giovanni da Verrazano was important to French exploration because

   Henry Hudson was important to Dutch and English exploration because

3. List the various effects of other European explorations. Your list should include at least four different effects. An example is done for you.
   - found rich resources of cod and other fish, which led European fishing boats to regularly visit the region
   •
   •
   •

1. Explain how exploration and trade contributed to the growth of capitalism in Europe during this time.

2. How does a *market economy* work?

3. What is a *cottage industry*? What effect did cottage industries have on capitalism?

4. What is *mercantilism*? What role did colonies play in this policy?

PROCESSING

Copy the T-chart below onto *a separate sheet of paper.* Then think about the various positive and negative effects of European exploration. Record at least eight effects, either positive or negative, on the appropriate side of the T-chart.

Examples of How Exploration Positively Affected the World	Examples of How Exploration Negatively Affected the World

Afterward, answer these questions below your chart:

- Overall, do you think the Age of Exploration had a more positive or a more negative impact on the world as a whole? Why?

- How did the Age of Exploration change the way Europeans viewed the world?

Preparing to Write: Analyzing Sources

Read the following excerpt from *The Devastation of the Indies: A Brief Account,* by Bartolomé de Las Casas, first published in 1552. Then answer the questions that follow.

The Indies were discovered in the year 1492. In the following year . . . many Spaniards went there with the intention of settling the land . . . [the] native peoples [are] called Indians . . . all the land so far discovered is a beehive of people . . . the goodness of the Indians is undeniable . . . [and] if this gifted people could be brought to know the one true God they would be the most fortunate people in the world.

Yet into this sheepfold [the Indians] . . . came some Spaniards who immediately behaved like ravening [greedy] wild beasts, wolves, tigers, or lions that had been starved for many days. And Spaniards have behaved in no other way during the past forty years . . . for they are still acting like . . . beasts, killing, terrorizing, afflicting, torturing, and destroying the native peoples . . . with the strangest and most varied new methods of cruelty, never seen or heard of before, and to such a degree that this Island of Hispaniola . . . having a population that I estimated to be more than three million, has now a population of barely two hundred persons.

List the main ideas of this excerpt.

1.

2.

3.

4.

5.

Circle the words that Las Casas used that captured your attention.

Do you think Las Casas wanted to inform or persuade others? Explain.

Writing a Weblog Entry

Today, many people write Weblogs, or blogs, to inform and persuade others about a point of view on an important issue. You will write a one-paragraph blog entry about a modern human-rights issue you think is important. Write your topic here.

Next, list the main ideas you want to cover in your blog entry.

1.

2.

3.

4.

5.

Finally, write your blog entry. Be sure it has a clear point of view and many details.

Use this rubric to evaluate your blog entry. Make changes to your blog entry if you need to.

Score	Description
3	The blog entry has a clear point of view and many details. It includes effective, persuasive words. It has no spelling or grammar errors.
2	The blog entry has a clear point of view and some details. It includes some persuasive words. It has some spelling or grammar errors.
1	The blog entry does not have a clear point of view and includes few details. It does not include any persuasive words. It has many spelling or grammar errors.

The Scientific Revolution

How did the Scientific Revolution change the way people understood the world?

In the space below, draw a diagram showing the relationship between the sun and the planets. Your diagram should include labels for the sun, each planet, and Earth's moon, and should show their orbits.

Key Content Terms

As you complete the Reading Notes, use these terms in your answers.

Scientific Revolution   heliocentric theory   scientific method

rationalism   gravity   hypothesis

geocentric theory   mass

Section 33.2

1. What two sources guided most Europeans' thinking about the natural world during the Middle Ages?

2. In two or three sentences, explain how each of the following led Europeans to question the traditional worldview:

   - Renaissance:

   - Age of Exploration:

Section 33.3

1. In the space below, complete a diagram that explains the heliocentric theory. Label the diagram with the three major parts of Copernicus's heliocentric theory.

2. How did Kepler's work improve on or support Copernicus's heliocentric theory?

Section 33.4

1. What were three important discoveries Galileo made with his telescope?

2. How did Galileo's discoveries help support the heliocentric theory?

3. Why did Catholic Church leaders feel threatened by Galileo's support of the heliocentric theory?

Section 33.5

1. What was the basic idea behind Newton's law of gravity?

2. How did Newton's work support the earlier work of Copernicus, Kepler, and Galileo?

Section 33.6

1. What role did Francis Bacon and Rene Descartes play in creating a new approach to science?

2. Complete the following chart by recording the steps of the scientific method. Include a symbol to represent each step.

Step	Symbol
1.	
2.	
3.	
4.	
5.	

In each box below, draw a quick sketch of each of the four key inventions of the Scientific Revolution covered in the chapter. Then write a one-sentence summary of each invention's purpose.

Telescope	Barometer
Microscope	**Thermometer**

Review and evaluate the importance of the discoveries, inventions, and contributions of the following individuals or groups of people during the Scientific Revolution:

- Nicolaus Copernicus and Johannes Kepler
- Galileo Galilei
- Francis Bacon and Rene Descartes
- Isaac Newton
- Antonie van Leeuwenhoek, Evangelista Torricelli, and Daniel Gabriel Fahrenheit

Then, using the awards pedestals below, award gold, silver, and bronze medals to the three individuals or groups you think did the most, during this time, to change the way people understand the world. On each pedestal, draw a picture or symbol to represent that winner. Then complete the sentence inside the appropriate pedestal for each medalist.

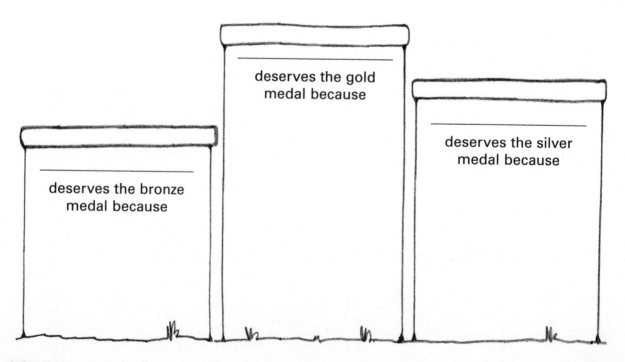

deserves the gold medal because

deserves the silver medal because

deserves the bronze medal because

The Enlightenment

How have the ideas of the Enlightenment influenced modern government?

Carefully analyze the image your teacher is projecting. As you discuss the questions below with your class, record your answers after each one.

- List four interesting details you see in this image.

  1.

  2.

  3.

  4.

- What conclusions can you draw about the people at this gathering? Give one piece of evidence to support each conclusion.

- What kinds of ideas might people discuss at a gathering like this, and why?

- In what ways might these people spread the ideas discussed at this gathering?

R E A D I N G   N O T E S

Key Content Terms

As you complete the Reading Notes, use these terms in your answers.

Enlightenment	social contract	despotism
constitutional monarchy	natural rights	religious tolerance
bill of rights	separation of powers	

Section 34.2

1. How are the ideas of the Scientific Revolution similar to the ideas of the Enlightenment?

2. In what ways did the Renaissance and the Reformation influence the Enlightenment?

3. Why did most Enlightenment philosophers continue to believe in God?

4. The new ideas of the Enlightenment clashed with some previously held beliefs about religion, morality, and government. Read the old beliefs shown on the T-chart below. Then write in the new ideas that developed during the Enlightenment.

Old Belief	New Idea
• Christian faith was based largely on trust in the Bible as God's word.	
• Ideas about right and wrong were based on religious teachings.	
• Kings had a divine right to rule.	

If your class is doing the activity for this chapter, complete each item for Sections 34.3 to 34.7. (*Note: If your class is not doing the activity, skip item 4 for each section.*)

Section 34.3

1. What were the major influences on Thomas Hobbes's thinking?

2. What major political arguments did Hobbes present in *Leviathan?*

3. What was Hobbes's lasting impact on government?

4. Hobbes was Enlightenment thinker _____. He said:

Section 34.4

1. What were the major influences on John Locke's thinking?

2. What major political arguments did Locke present in *Two Treatises of Government?*

3. What was Locke's lasting impact on government?

4. Locke was Enlightenment thinker _____. He said:

Section 34.5

1. What were the major influences on Baron de Montesquieu's thinking?

2. What major political arguments did Montesquieu present in
    The Spirit of Laws?

3. What was Montesquieu's lasting impact on government?

4. Montesquieu was Enlightenment thinker _____. He said:

Section 34.6

1. What were the major influences on Voltaire's thinking?

2. What major political arguments did Voltaire present in his writings?

3. What was Voltaire's lasting impact on government?

4. Voltaire was Enlightenment thinker _____. He said:

Section 34.7

1. What were the major beliefs that influenced Cesare Beccaria's thinking?

2. What major political arguments did Beccaria present in *On Crimes and Punishments?*

3. What was Beccaria's lasting impact on government?

4. Beccaria was Enlightenment thinker _____. He said:

Section 34.8

1. Who were some of Europe's "enlightened despots"? What types of reforms did these rulers introduce?

2. Which Enlightenment thinkers' ideas were reflected in the following U.S. documents? List the name of the Enlightenment thinker(s), and what ideas of his were included in the document. (For example, Voltaire: free speech.)

- Declaration of Independence:

- Constitution:

- Bill of Rights:

Section 34.9

How did each of the following women contribute to the Enlightenment?

- Madame Geoffrin:

- Abigail Adams:

- Olympe de Gouges:

- Mary Wollstonecraft:

PROCESSING

Find a newspaper article or photograph that you think represents an idea of one of the Enlightenment thinkers you studied. Highlight or circle any specific parts of the article or photograph that relate to the Enlightenment idea. Glue the article onto *a separate sheet of paper,* and then complete the following statement beneath your article or photo:

This article or photograph represents _____(name of thinker)'s_____ Enlightenment idea of _____(idea)_____ because

Timeline Skills

Analyze the Unit 8 timeline in your book. Also think about what you have learned in this unit. Then answer the following questions.

1. How many years after Columbus reached the Americas did Spain finish conquering the Aztec and Inca empires?

2. In what century did the prices of Asian goods drop in Europe, and what caused the drop?

3. Name three new scientific tools that were developed during the Scientific Revolution.

4. Why was Copernicus's heliocentric theory significant?

5. What was important about the English defeat of the Spanish Armada?

6. How did salons help to shape and spread the ideas of the Enlightenment?

7. Which scientist's important astronomical discoveries put him in conflict with the Catholic Church?

8. Why were Newton's laws of motion and gravity important?

9. What was Locke's argument about government?

10. What political upheavals resulted from Enlightenment ideas? When did each happen?

Critical Thinking

Use the timeline and the chapters in the unit to answer the following questions.

11. Which theory, law, discovery, or invention during the Scientific Revolution do you think was most significant, and why?

12. When the newly independent United States of America wrote its Constitution in 1787, one of the key features of the new government was the establishment of an executive branch, a legislative branch, and a judicial branch. What Enlightenment philosophy does that represent, and which European thinker proposed it?

13. Compare and contrast exploration by Portugal, Spain, and England during the Age of Exploration.

14. If you could add three more events to this timeline, which would they be? List each event, and explain why you think it is important enough to add to the timeline.

    a.

    b.

    c.

Chapter 21
161: Ellis Amdur, "Women Warrior of Japan," *Journal of Asian Martial Arts* 5, no. 2, (1996), at http://www.koryu.com.

Chapter 28
216: Niccolò Machiavelli, *The Prince,* trans. Luigi Ricci (London: Grant Richards, 1903). Niccolò Machiavelli, in Peter Loptson, ed., *Readings on Human Nature* (Orchard Park, NY: Broadview Press, 1998). Ibid.

Chapter 32
253: Bartolomé de las Casas, in Howard Zinn and Anthony Arnove, *Voices of a People's History of the United States,* 2nd ed. (New York: Seven Stories Press, 2009).

Photographs

Cover: Gina Martin/Getty Images

Title page: Gina Martin/Getty Images

Chapter 4
23: Bettmann/Corbis

Chapter 6
40L: Jose F. Poblete/Corbis 40R: Alexander Burkatovski/Corbis

Chapter 8
55TL: Mikhail Levit/Shutterstock 55ML: Peter Sanders Photography 55BL: Peter Sanders Photography 55TR: Aleksandar Kamasi/Shutterstock 55BR: Majedali | Dreamstime.com

Chapter 11
81L: Joseph Sohm-Visions of America/Getty Images 81R: Greenshoots Communications/Alamy

Chapter 13
93: Marc and Evelyn Bernheim/Woodfin Camp & Associates

Chapter 28
211: Radius Images/Photolibrary 218TL: Bill Ross/Corbis 218TC: iStockphoto.com 218BL: Francis G. Mayer/Corbis 218BC: British Museum, London/Bridgeman Art Library 218BR: Shutterstock

Art

Chapter 2
11: Doug Roy 14–15: Len Ebert

Chapter 3
21: Len Ebert

Chapter 4
28: Doug Roy

Chapter 5
34: Susan Jaekel

Chapter 8
60: Doug Roy

Chapter 10
69: Renate Lohmann

Chapter 12
89: Len Ebert 91–92: Len Ebert

Chapter 13
98: Doug Roy

Chapter 14
101: Doug Roy

Chapter 17
126-128: Doug Roy

Chapter 18
129-132: Len Ebert

Chapter 19
145-148: Len Ebert

Chapter 20
150: Len Ebert 156-159: Len Ebert

Chapter 22
172: Doug Roy 173: Doug Roy

Chapter 23
175: Renate Lohmann

Chapter 27
205: Susan Jaekel 210: Susan Jaekel

Chapter 28
213: Susan Jaekel

Chapter 29
221–225: Rosiland Solomon 226: Vicki Philp

Chapter 30
234: Doug Roy